SOUND WAVES AND LIGHT WAVES

An unusually varied career in engineering and science supported the writing of SOUND WAVES AND LIGHT WAVES. Besides contributing to acoustics, radar, solid-state physics, and television, Winston E. Kock built one of the first electronic organs and helped to create a computer that could recognize sounds of speech.

Designing the electronic organ, in 1932, was the project for Kock's senior thesis in Electrical Engineering at the University of Cincinnati, where he also received the M.S. degree in physics the following year. From Cincinnati he went to the University of Berlin, in Germany, which bestowed the Ph.D. degree in Physics *cum laude* on him in 1934. At Berlin he came in contact with Max Planck and Max von Laue, two of the great men in science in the early years of this century. He later attended the Institute for Advanced Study at Princeton, New Jersey, after a year as a teaching fellow at Cincinnati, and there took courses under Albert Einstein, John von Neumann, and Eugene Wigner, among others. He spent a summer at the Indian Institute of Science at Bangalore, India, studying under Sir C. V. Raman, a Nobel laureate.

Dr. Kock devoted several years to the development of a commercial version of his organ for the Baldwin Piano Company, at Cincinnati. In 1942 he joined the Radio Research Department of Bell Telephone Laboratories at Holmdel, New Jersey, where he worked, under Harald T. Friis, on microwave lenses which eventually were to go into the Bell System's coast-to-coast microwave relay circuits. He transferred to the Bell Murray Hill Labs in 1948 to work in acoustics and on the transistor (he holds a joint patent on the coaxial transistor). He became Director of Acoustics Research at Bell Labs, invented several lenses for loudspeakers, and worked on the computer for speech recognition. He also directed research on a narrow-band TV transmission system based on acoustic techniques. In 1956 he joined the Bendix Corporation and subsequently became its Vice-President—Research, in Detroit, Michigan. On September 1, 1964, Dr. Kock became director of the new NASA Electronics Research Center.

Dr. Kock lives in Ann Arbor, Michigan. For hobbies he plays the piano and organ and raises orchids, having named one for his wife and another for one of their three children. He received an honorary doctor of science degree in 1952 from the University of Cincinnati, and Eta Kappa Nu, the honorary electrical engineering society, has given him several awards. He has been on the Governing Board of the American Institute of Physics for the past six years. He holds more than eighty patents.

Sound Waves and
Light Waves

BY WINSTON E. KOCK

Published by Anchor Books

Doubleday & Company, Inc.
Garden City, New York

THE SCIENCE STUDY SERIES

The Science Study Series offers to students and to the general public the writing of distinguished authors on the most stirring and fundamental topics of science, from the smallest known particles to the whole universe. Some of the books tell of the role of science in the world of man, his technology and civilization. Others are biographical in nature, telling the fascinating stories of the great discoverers and their discoveries. All the authors have been selected both for expertness in the fields they discuss and for ability to communicate their special knowledge and their own views in an interesting way. The primary purpose of these books is to provide a survey within the grasp of the young student or the layman. Many of the books, it is hoped, will encourage the reader to make his own investigations of natural phenomena.

The Series, which now offers topics in all the sciences and their applications, had its beginning in a project to revise the secondary schools' physics curriculum. At the Massachusetts Institute of Technology during 1956 a group of physicists, high school teachers, journalists, apparatus designers, film producers, and other specialists organized the Physical Science Study Committee, now operating as a part of Educational Services Incorporated, Watertown, Massachusetts. They pooled their knowledge and experience toward the design and creation of aids to the learning of physics. Initially their effort was supported by the National Science Foundation, which has continued to aid the program. The Ford Foundation, the Fund for the Advancement of Education, and the Alfred P. Sloan Foundation have also given support. The Committee has created a textbook, an extensive film series, a laboratory guide, especially designed apparatus, and a teachers' source book.

The Series is guided by a Board of Editors consisting of Bruce F. Kingsbury, Managing Editor; John H. Durston, General Editor; Paul R. Brandwein, the Conservation Foundation and Harcourt, Brace & World, Inc.; Samuel A. Goudsmit, Brookhaven National Laboratory; Philippe LeCorbeiller, Harvard University; and Gerard Piel, *Scientific American*.

FOREWORD

In elementary physics there is a classic demonstration of an important property of light. A narrow beam of light from some sort of lantern or projector enters a glass-walled box filled with smoke. We can see the beam because the smoke particles randomly reflect (or scatter) some of the light to our eyes. On the bottom of the box is a shiny reflecting surface, say a glass mirror. When the beam strikes the mirror and is reflected, it forms a sharp "V" in the smoke, with its apex on the mirror. Even without making a precise measurement, we can see *with our own eyes* that some simple relationship must exist between the angle at which the beam approaches the mirror and the angle at which it leaves the mirror.

A line drawn (or imagined) perpendicular to the mirror at the point of the "V" is called the *normal,* and if we look at the two legs of the "V" in relation to the perpendicular, it is apparent that the angle formed between the approaching beam and this normal is equal to the angle formed between the normal and the reflected beam. Now, we would have had no difficulty memorizing the law that the *angle of incidence* is equal to the *angle of reflection,* and if we had a taste for Euclidean geometry, we could, on the basis of this law alone, derive mathematical relationships between beams of light and surfaces of various shapes. But our feelings about memorized laws and about the "V" we can see with our own eyes are quite different. The memorized law is an abstraction, which we are willing to accept in proper respect for recognized authority, but the sharp "V" glowing in the smoke-filled box is reality, never to be forgotten. In watching this demonstration we have made at least one law of the physics concerning light a part of ourselves.

The vast majority of the civilized world today use the phrases "light waves," "radio waves," "sound waves" quite casually. It would be remarkable if they did not. More and more, our society lives by devices whose operations depend on wave behavior. But these devices have become extremely complicated and involve laws of light (and of sound) that cannot be reduced to such simple demonstrations as the experiment described. Still, it is possible to portray a good many of these more intricate properties of light and sound in easily understood visual presentations, and it is the purpose of this book to conduct the reader on what we might call a guided tour of such demonstrations. It will not be beyond the resources of many readers to duplicate a number of the demonstrations for themselves, but it is the author's hope, and intention, that every reader will be able to get from the drawings and photographs and the accompanying discussions a measure of the same confidence that is inspired by watching the experiment of the reflected beam of light. While the book's fundamental aim, of course, is to explain various aspects of wave behavior by showing them in operation in experimental situations that can be pictured, it offers as an extra dividend (or so the author hopes) explanations of several advanced and rather important technological devices.

It may come as a surprise to some readers that we should have coupled sound and light together in the same sentence. They are two totally different phenomena, of course, one perceived by our sense of sight, the other by our sense of hearing. Sound waves constitute mechanical motions of air particles, whereas light waves are electromagnetic in nature. Yet they have one important thing in common: both are forms of wave motion. It is interesting to discover how much we can learn about electromagnetic waves by observing the properties of sound waves (and the other way around, of course). We shall see that both waves can be portrayed visually by means of the same technique,* and we shall find that there are lenses and prisms that can focus and refract both sound waves and electromagnetic waves simultaneously. We shall learn that a distinguished British physicist, Lord Rayleigh (1842–1919), in several instances analyzed scattering and diffraction problems in general form first (grouping together what he called "aerial" waves and "electrical" waves), and later in the analysis singled out special cases that pertained to only one or the other of the two types.

One purpose of this book is to illustrate similarities between sound waves and light waves and to show how the knowledge of the behavior of one can aid us in our understanding of the other. It is hoped that this process may demonstrate in a small way the usefulness of comparisons in scientific

---

* All the photographs portraying sound waves and microwaves were taken by F. K. Harvey of the Bell Telephone Laboratories. The author wishes to thank Mr. Harvey for permitting use of them.

thought. As we learn of new developments in one field of science we can often apply the same concepts in another, unrelated, field. To do this well we must train ourselves to think about similarities that exist, even remotely, between the two fields. Lord Rayleigh was one scientist who employed comparisons or analogs very successfully; there were and are many others like him. One must have the will to acquire knowledge in several fields; extreme specialization does not lend itself to analog thinking. Most of our truly great scientists today continue to maintain broad interests in many fields.

To encourage the habit of "comparison thinking," our text will *not* be divided into chapters on sound and chapters on electromagnetic waves. Instead, both subjects will be discussed together. We shall first examine the fundamental properties of wave motion. Following this we shall interest ourselves in the representation of sound waves and light waves in pictorial form. Finally, we shall consider various analogs between the two wave types.

CONTENTS

SOUND WAVES AND LIGHT WAVES

Chapter I

WAVE MOTION

Water Waves

Wave motion must figure in the earliest memories of us all. Who among us, from the time he was first able to stagger about on his own legs, did not toss a pebble or heave a rock into every body of water he passed? Or splash in the bathtub? The peculiarly satisfying "ker-plonk!" sound probably was the original attraction, but watching the waves created by the pebble or rock quickly became the main pleasure. The symmetrical patterns appeal to something basic in the human mind. The waves roll outward from the splash of the rock in ever widening circles, traveling at constant speed across the water, eventually to die out (if the pond or lake is large enough) or to reflect from the banks or other obstacles.

The "ker-plonk!" involved wave motion too, we learned when we grew old enough to go to school. All the phenomena perceived with our eyes as light and with our ears as sound are as truly forms of wave motion as are the water waves rolling away from the rock as it enters the pond. The waves of light and sound are not so easily made real to us as are water waves, because their motion occurs not on the two-dimensional surface of a pond, but in three-dimensional space. Nevertheless, for a beginning, we can become acquainted with the properties

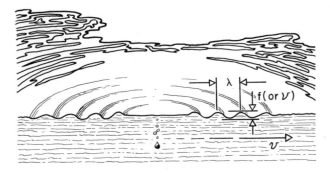

FIG. 1. Water waves on a pond. The speed v is called the velocity of propagation, the distance from crest to crest the wavelength λ, and the periodicity of the up-and-down motion of a point on the surface is called frequency f (or ν).

of all wave motion by studying the properties exhibited before our eyes by water waves.

We noted that the waves produced by the pebble move out at constant speed. This wave speed (Figure 1) is called the *velocity of propagation*. The waves themselves have crests and troughs, points where the water level is elevated and points where the level of the water is depressed. The surface undulates rhythmically between crest and trough, crest and trough. The distance between successive crests or troughs is called the wavelength. It is usually denoted by the Greek letter λ (lambda). As the waves move past a given point on the surface of the water in the pond, they cause an up-and-down motion of the water at this point. This up-and-down motion is repeated in time in a periodic manner, and the rate in times per second with which this up-and-down motion repeats itself is re-

ferred to as the frequency of the wave. It is denoted by f, or by the Greek letter ν (nu).

We shall now examine in further detail these
three fundamental aspects of wave motion: (1) the
velocity with which the wave proceeds onward or
propagates, (2) the distance between crests or
troughs (that is, the wavelength), and (3) the
periodicity or frequency, that attribute of the wave
which specifies the rate at which the medium pul-
sates to and fro.

Wave Velocity

When we see someone at a distance hitting an
object with a hammer or creating a loud noise in
some other way that involves visible physical movement, we notice that there is a lapse of time between our sighting the action and our hearing the
noise. It takes longer for the sound to arrive at our
ears than for the sight to arrive at our eyes. Sound
travels at a definite velocity. In air this velocity (at
sea level) is about 1100 feet per second. A noise
created 1100 feet away would take one second to
get to our ears.

Light waves, however, travel at an almost unbe-
lievable speed, 186,000 miles per second. Accordingly, any event on earth that we can see at all
seems to have happened at the instant we see it.
The light from a lightning flash miles away reaches
our eyes in so small a fraction of a second that
the propagation delay is unnoticeable. Not so, however, for the thunder created by the lightning. From
the velocity figure of 1100 feet per second we see
that the delay here may be many seconds. This

relationship between the extremely high speed of travel of the lightning flash and the much lower speed of travel of the thunderclap permits us to calculate how far away a thunderstorm is. If the elapsed time between our seeing the flash and hearing the thunder is greater than five seconds, we know that the storm is more than a mile away.

Both types of waves have been used for sending messages from one point to another, but from velocity considerations we see that communicating with light (as by flashing a beam of sunlight with a mirror toward a receiving point) constitutes a much more rapid means than one using sound waves (as by drums or other audible signaling methods).

Wavelength

When we consider the wavelengths involved in sound waves and light waves, we again find wide differences. The sound waves we can hear have wavelengths ranging from about ¾ inch at the highest-pitched tones to perhaps 50 feet at the very lowest audible tones. The electromagnetic waves that we can see—that is, those in the visible range of the electromagnetic spectrum—have wavelengths ranging from about 16 millionths of an inch at the violet end to about 38 millionths of an inch at the red end.

In both hearing and seeing, our limited powers of perception prevent us from perceiving wavelengths beyond the limits mentioned. Nevertheless, we do know from measurements that there exist both sound waves and electromagnetic waves having wavelengths well beyond these limits. In the field of sound we divide the waves into three categories: (1) the infrasonic or subaudible range, (2) the sonic range, and (3) the ultrasonic range.

In the field of electromagnetic waves, we have a larger number of categories: (1) radio waves, (2) infrared, (3) visible, (4) ultraviolet, (5) X rays and (6) gamma rays. The radio waves have the longest wavelengths; the shortest waves in this category, those called microwaves, merge with the longest infrared waves. Similarly, the shortest infrared waves merge with the red visible waves, the shortest visible violet waves merge with the longest ultraviolet waves, and so on. The visible spectrum ranges from red through orange, yellow, green, blue, and violet, and at this point the ultraviolet range begins. Beyond the ultraviolet the electromagnetic spectrum extends from the soft X-ray region on into the shortest wavelength region of all, that of gamma rays.

Frequency

If we divide the wave *velocity* (expressed in feet per second) by the wave*length* (expressed in feet), the length term (feet) cancels out, and the result must be expressed as "something per second." We call this result "frequency" because it states how frequently new wave crests pass a given point. We express it in terms of "cycles per second" because it tells us how many wave troughs and wave crests (how many cycles) pass the given point in one second.

We can rewrite "velocity divided by wavelength equals frequency" as

Frequency times wavelength=velocity   (1)

This equality says that since the velocity is constant (1100 feet a second for sound, 186,000 miles a second for light or other electromagnetic waves), a wave with a small wavelength has a high frequency and one with a long wavelength a low frequency. Since we know the velocity, we can always calculate from equation (1) the frequency required by a certain wavelength, or the other way around. Thus, for a sound wave to have a wavelength of 1 foot, the frequency must be 1100 cycles per second. For an electromagnetic wave to have a wavelength of 1 mile, the frequency must be 186,000 cycles per second.

Using the wavelength limits quoted, let us, as an exercise, calculate the frequencies of sound waves we can hear and those of the electromagnetic waves we can see. We will use the symbol f to denote frequency. A sound wave having a wavelength of ¾ inch would have a frequency

$$f = \frac{1100 \times 12}{3/4} = 17,600 \text{ cycles per second}$$

Some people, and most animals, can hear higher frequencies than this, but older people usually have a lower limit of hearing than this figure.

The 50-foot wavelength sound wave has a frequency

$$f = \frac{1100}{50} = 22 \text{ cycles per second}$$

Some organ pipes generate vibrations as low as 16 cycles per second, but there is some argument whether we really *hear* (rather than *feel*) such low frequency sound waves.

We stated that violet light has a wavelength of about 16 millionths of an inch. To express the velocity of light in inches per second we must multiply 186,000 by the number of feet in a mile (5280) and the number of inches in a foot (12). Our expression for frequency then becomes

$$f = \frac{186,000 \times 5280 \times 12}{16/1,000,000}$$

$$= 737,000,000,000,000 \text{ cycles per second}$$

or $f = 7.37 \times 10^{14}$ cycles per second*

At the red end the waves have a frequency of

$$f = \frac{186,000 \times 5280 \times 12}{38/1,000,000}$$

$$= 3.11 \times 10^{14} \text{ cycles per second}$$

A Short Diversion

The relationship (1) gives us a hint of how we might design lenses that can focus sound waves and electromagnetic waves at the same time. We shall describe such lenses in detail later, but let us think briefly about the possibility. We consider first the fact that the focusing ability of a lens is set by its size as measured in wavelengths. Thus a 200-inch telescope for light waves is more powerful than a 100-inch one. Similarly, as shown in Figure 2, a lens with a diameter of a certain number of wavelengths will create the same focused beam pattern for sound waves as for electromagnetic waves.

For the *same* lens to act identically for both sound and electromagnetic waves, however, the wave-*lengths* of the two waves must be identical. Is there a region of the two spectra where this condition

---

* In the exponential notation 10^{14} is shorthand for a one followed by fourteen zeros. 10^{-14} is the inverse, or $1/10^{14}$. Use of this notation for very large and very small numbers is accepted practice in science.

8

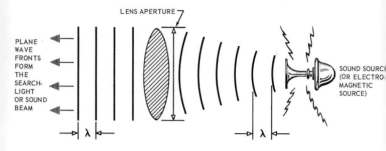

Fig. 2. A lens of a given aperture in terms of wavelengths will create the same beam whether sound or electromagnetic energy is involved.

exists? Of course, there are many, but one region is important from a practical standpoint. This is the region where the wavelengths run from one to three inches. In acoustics this is the range of great interest to hi-fi enthusiasts, covering frequencies from about 4500 cycles to 13,200 cycles per second. In electromagnetics it covers a part of the microwave spectrum of great importance to telephone and television communication networks, to radar, and to satellite communications. The same lens, if effective for both types of waves, could be used interchangeably (or simultaneously) in both sets of applications. Again as an exercise, let us calculate the differences in frequency for a sound wave an inch in wavelength and an electromagnetic wave an inch in wavelength. From equation (1) for sound waves we have

$$f = \frac{1100 \times 12}{1} = 13,200 \text{ cycles per second}$$

For light waves we have

$$f = \frac{186,000 \times 5280 \times 12}{1}$$
$$= 11,800,000,000 \text{ cycles per second}$$
or 11.8 kilomegacycles per second†

The wide difference in frequency of the two waves combined with the wide difference in velocity permits, by virtue of equation (1), both wavelengths to be one inch. For dual use of a lens it is fortunate that the focusing action depends upon the *wavelength* rather than the velocity or frequency.

Longitudinal (Compressional) Waves

Let us consider next various types of wave motion. Figure 3 shows a long, coiled spring stretched

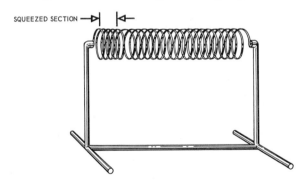

SQUEEZED SECTION

FIG. 3. When a few loops of a long, coiled spring are squeezed together and then released, the impulse thus created travels along the axis of the spring in the form of a longitudinal, or compressional, wave.

† The frequency units for high frequencies are: a thousand cycles equals a kilocycle, a million cycles equals a megacycle, and a thousand million cycles equals a kilomegacycle, or gigacycle.

between two supports. If we compress a few loops at one end and suddenly let go, the disturbance thus created will move from that end to the other and back again several times until it finally dies out. If we are careful, we can make this impulse travel without any vertical or sideways motion of the spring; in other words, we can make the motion of the disturbance purely *longitudinal*.

Because the disturbance that actually moves is a compression of the coils, such longitudinal waves are also called compressional waves. At the top of Figure 4 we see the instantaneous pattern of the moving disturbance with its compressed and expanded sections of the coiled spring. Beneath it we have plotted the variation in amount of compression (the "density" of loops per unit of length). This

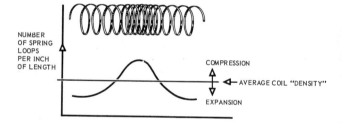

F<small>IG</small>. 4. *Top*: Instantaneous picture of the compressional
        wave on the spring of F<small>IG</small>. 3.
        Bottom: Plotting the number of coils per inch of
        length helps to show the resemblance of the com-
        pressional wave to a water wave.

curve shows that the compressional wave also possesses a wavelike character similar to the water waves discussed earlier.

Sound waves are compressional waves. When we strike a kettledrum we momentarily push the stretched skin inward. The skin moves so rapidly the air above the drumhead cannot follow in the downward motion. The blow thus creates a partial vacuum in the immediate vicinity of the drumhead just as we created a compressed section of spring in the coiled spring of Figure 3. The air reacts to this disturbance just as the coiled spring did, and the region of lower air density travels outward from the drum in the same way the disturbance of higher "coil density" moved down the coiled springs. The air experiences density variations just as the spring had coil densities that were lower and higher than the average.

We show this effect in Figure 4. Just as the pebble creates a small group of waves (a wave "train") on the pond, so the striking of the kettledrum generates a group of sound waves as the drum skin vibrates. As these waves travel outward from the drum, they produce regions of lower and higher air density, depicted in Figure 5 by the concentration of the small dots. Because the sound from the drum travels outward in all directions, these high and low density regions are concentric spheres having a common center at the drum. This spherical propagation is a consequence of the fact that sound waves are three-dimensional. The waves on the coiled spring are one-dimensional; water waves are two-dimensional.

Transverse Waves

Everyone has twitched the end of a rope (Figure 6) to make a wave travel up and down it. Such a wave moves rapidly. A similar effect can be obtained with a length of garden hose stretched out on the ground. One sudden jerk causes a visible disturbance to travel the length of the hose. We see in Figure 6 that the wave gives each point of the rope an up-and-down motion which is perpendicular to

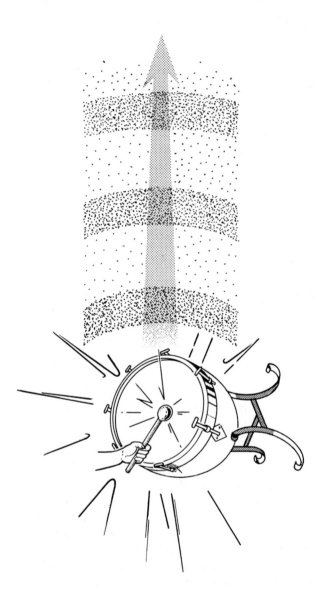

Fig. 5. Instantaneous air-density pattern caused by the compressional sound waves radiated by a kettledrum.

the line of the rope. In contrast to the motion of the coiled spring, we are dealing now with *transverse* waves rather than longitudinal ones. Here the transverse motion lies in a vertical plane. Had we made the generating motion a side-to-side one, however, we could have caused the transverse rope movement to lie wholly in a horizontal plane. We could refer, in these two situations, to the waves as being *plane polarized* (or linearly polarized), since in both the motion remains within a given plane. The waves of the first situation (Figure 6) would be called *vertically polarized* and the side-to-side waves would be called *horizontally polarized*. *Polarization* is the general term.

If we imparted a circular motion to the end of the rope in Figure 6 (as though we were rapidly turning a crank), we would see a spiraling motion travel

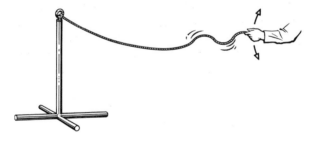

FIG. 6. Transverse waves on a stretched clothesline created by a rapid up-and-down motion at one end.

down the rope. If we watched the shadow this wave motion cast on a vertical wall, we would see that it looked much like the vertically polarized waves we previously generated. But if we watched a shadow of this spiraling wave on the floor, we would get the idea that the wave on the rope was a side-to-side or horizontally polarized wave.

In other words, we can look upon the spiral wave as a combination of two plane-polarized waves. Or, equally well, we can think of the spiral wave as a plane-polarized wave whose plane of polarization continuously *rotates* as the wave propagates forward. For this reason, such a wave is called a *circularly polarized* wave.

Electromagnetic waves are transverse waves. They can be generated by a rapid alternation of the direction of electric current flow in a conducting wire. The tall tower of a radio broadcasting station constitutes such a wire, and if a current of rapidly varying direction is caused to flow in the tower, electromagnetic waves are radiated in all directions of the compass. These waves are vertically polarized because the tower is vertical. For television broadcasting shorter wavelength radio waves are used, and in the United States horizontal polarization is considered superior. Our television receiving antennas are therefore horizontal rods (rather than vertical) and because of the short wavelengths involved, the antennas need be only a few feet long. In England vertical polarization was thought best for television, and there the forests of TV antennas on city rooftops are vertical.

Polarization of Light

Since light waves are electromagnetic waves, they too are polarized. They are also generated electrically, usually by the rapid up-and-down or side-to-side motion of myriads of the tiny electrically charged particles called electrons. Because electrons can move in just about any direction, light waves from most light sources are *randomly* polarized. Polarized light can easily be produced, however, by the simple process of filtering out all waves except those polarized in a given desired plane. One way is to pass the light through a sheet of Polaroid. This material transmits only waves polarized in one particular plane; it absorbs all others.

Since the visual process that occurs in our eyes is not sensitive to the direction of polarization of light waves, it is not too easy to demonstrate visually the polarized properties of light. If we look through two sheets of polaroid, one on top of the other, we see how the light is affected. If the sheets are similarly oriented, we can see through both sheets together since both are transmitting waves of one particular polarization. If we turn one sheet around 90° and try to look through both, we find that they are now opaque. The first sheet has passed waves of one polarization, but the second is oriented so as to absorb those coming through the first.

When randomly polarized sunlight strikes obliquely on the surface of a body of water, a large fraction of the vertically polarized waves is absorbed, whereas the horizontally polarized waves are almost completely reflected. The *reflected* light is therefore strongly polarized in the horizontal direction. Polaroid sunglasses cause this strong horizontal component to be absorbed, and the glare from the water surface is thereby reduced appreciably.

Chapter II

THE WAVE NATURE OF
SOUND AND LIGHT

Though we have examined, in Chapter I, some properties of wave motion and related them to sound and light, we have yet to demonstrate that sound and light really do propagate as waves. Perhaps we can find some technique of visual presentation that will convince us that sound and light are waves.

How to proceed? Sound itself is not visible. Light, though visible, consists of frequencies so high we could not possibly follow the wave motion with our eyes. Suppose, for a beginning, that we could not actually see water waves. How could we go about proving that they do exist?

Portraying Water Waves

First, we would need a situation in which water waves were being produced continually, say on the surface of a large pond. The pebble of Figure 1 caused some waves on the pond but not enough for us to study them. Figure 7, showing a cross section of the pond at the surface, illustrates an apparatus suitable to our experiment. The mechanism moves a plunger up and down continuously, creating water waves of constant amplitude (height) for an indefinite period of time. At the right of Figure 7 we see a cork bobber floating on the water surface. As the waves pass the cork, it bobs up and down in syn-

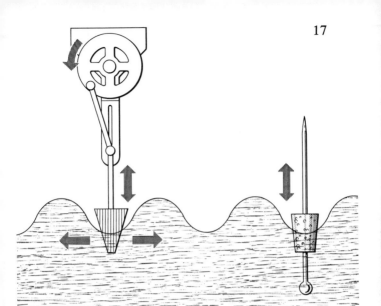

Fig. 7. Outward-traveling water waves are produced continuously by means of a plunger mechanism. The motion of the cork bobber indicates presence of waves and shows their magnitude.

chronism with the wave-generating mechanism. Consequently the motion of the bobber can be considered an indication of a disturbance of the originally smooth surface of the pond, and the height of the bobber's motion can indicate something of the magnitude of this disturbance. If the motion is small, the disturbance must be small; if the motion is large, the disturbance is large. A motionless bobber would tell us that there is no disturbance at all.

Let us now attach a pencil to the bobber (Figure 8) and rig a piece of cardboard perpendicular to the water's surface where the pencil will make marks on it when the bobber rises or falls. Gentle waves will leave short pencil marks on the card;

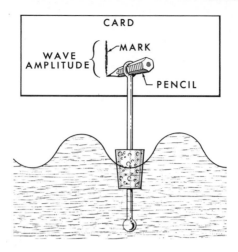

CARD

WAVE AMPLITUDE { MARK

PENCIL

FIG. 8. Pencil attached to a floating bobber could mark a record of the wave amplitude on a fixed card.

waves of greater amplitude will produce longer ones. We have in principle devised an apparatus (although a cumbersome and rather impractical one) for making a visual record of the magnitude of the water disturbance. Bobbers located a great distance away from the wave-generating mechanism would show, by their smaller marks, that a disturbance dies down in the course of its travel. We could transfer the magnitudes of the marks made by bobbers in many locations to a chart and thereby obtain a sort of map on which would be plotted the wave amplitude everywhere on the pond.

But we still have not shown on our hypothetical cards, or on the hypothetical chart, the *wave* nature of the water disturbance. Suppose now that we try to picture how two adjacent corks would move in relation to the plunger of the wave-creating mechanism. As shown in Figure 9, both would move up and down, but one would move up when the plunger moved up, whereas the other (a half wavelength

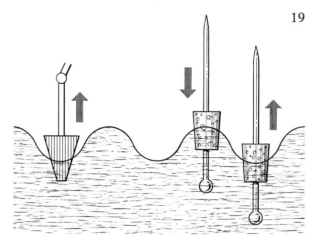

Fig. 9. At certain points on the pond a floating object moves up when the plunger moves up. At other points objects move oppositely.

away) would move down. Figure 9 pictures one instant of time in the wave motion; the plunger is shown at the lower end of its stroke and the far bobber is likewise at its lowest point. For the closer bobber (a half wavelength closer) the position is reversed; this bobber is at its highest point when the plunger is at its lowest point.

Now let us attach pencils to the two bobbers of Figure 9 and use a card firmly fastened to the plunger mechanism (Figure 10) instead of the stationary card we used earlier. As the pencil on bobber A moves up and down, the card moves up and down with it, and the A pencil will therefore not make a mark on the card. Bobber B, on the other hand, moves down when the card moves up, and up when the card moves down. Its pencil makes a long mark on the card. Let us now increase the number of bobbers to five; the card then appears as in Figure 11. For a still larger number the marks on the card would appear as in Figure 12.

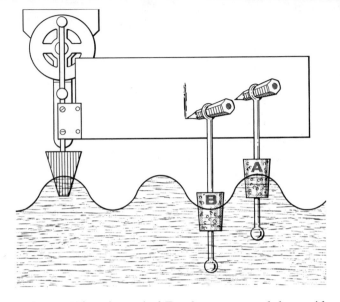

Fig. 10. When the card of Fig. 8 moves up and down with the plunger mechanism, bobbers that move in synchronism make no marks whereas those moving oppositely do.

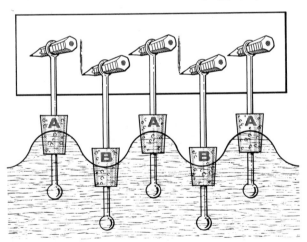

Fig. 11. If a multiplicity of bobbers and pencils were used as in Fig. 10, successive points of zero amplitude (points A), and maximum amplitude (points B) could be drawn.

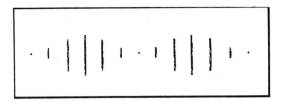

FIG. 12. A large number of bobbers in the arrangement of Figure 10 could plot a wave shape as shown here and thus would give an accurate measure of wavelength.

In Figure 12 the outline of the water wave is beginning to take shape. We have created, by the use of a moving card and bobbers with pencils, a faithful picture of the water wave. The picture is convincing evidence that there are waves on the water surface. It also gives us a measure of the wavelength of the waves (the distance between the crests or between the troughs).

"Seeing" Sound Waves

Perhaps our technique of plotting the outlines of water waves with bobbers and pencils has an analog that could enable us to display sound waves and electromagnetic waves. Pictures of these types of disturbance could show us then that both processes are also forms of wave motion. From the pictures or plots we might also get some information about the wave properties (such as wavelength). The bobbers, we recall, were in fact devices which detected and measured the amplitude of the water waves. Accordingly we must seek devices that can detect and measure the strength of sound waves or light waves. Let us start with sound waves.

Our approach will be to employ some mechanism or device that not only will detect sound but also will convert the sound energy into something we can see. We converted the water wave motion into pencil marks on cards, thereby displaying on the cards the waves and their magnitude. In sound waves the rapidity of vibration rules out any mechanical possibilities. We have devices, however, that can convert sounds into electrical signals. These devices, called microphones, convert varying sound pressure into a varying electric current. They are widely used in radio and television broadcasting, in telephone communication, and in making phonograph records and tape recordings. Microphones are also able to "recognize" the intensity, or amplitude, of sound waves. The louder the sound (that is, the greater the amplitude of the wave) the larger will be the electric current produced in the microphone. Suppose we connect a microphone (through its appropriate electrical amplifier) not to a telephone circuit or tape recorder, but to a light bulb. A neon lamp is best for this purpose because it responds much more rapidly than an incandescent lamp. The brightness of the neon light is an indication (Figure 13) of the loudness of the sound received at the microphone, and corresponds to the length of the mark on the card of the pencil-equipped bobber. Both are measures of the magnitude of the waves being detected.

Let us use this technique to generate a visual representation of a particular sound wave pattern. One sound pattern of interest might be that produced by a horn or bugle. Following the earlier method of the multiple bobbers, we could use a large number of microphones to generate the pattern, each microphone having its own amplifier and light bulb. As suggested by the three examples in Figure 14, we would create thereby a pattern of lights similar to the multiple marks formed by many pencil-equipped bobbers.

A simpler method, however, is shown in Figure

LOUD SOUND BRIGHT LIGHT

SOFT SOUND DIM LIGHT

FIG. 13. A microphone, which converts sound signals to electrical signals, gives a visual indication of sound intensity when hooked up with an amplifier and light bulb. Above, loud sound (large electrical signal) produces bright light; below, weaker sound produces a dimmer light.

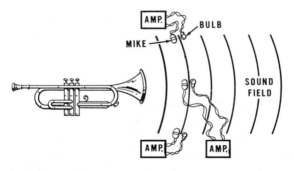

FIG. 14. A large number of microphone-light combinations (only three are shown) could portray the pattern of the sound intensity in a given space.

15. It requires one microphone, one amplifier, and one light affixed to the microphone. The microphone-light combination is moved about in the sound field created by a horn loudspeaker. The light becomes bright where the sound is loud, and dim where the sound is weak. The sound field is maintained continuously (we used the plunger mechanism to maintain the continuous field of water waves) by connecting the horn loudspeaker to an electrical oscillator producing a continuous electrical signal. The experiment is performed in the dark. A camera is set at time exposure (lens shutter continuously open) and aimed at the region of the sound field we are exploring. As the microphone equipped with light bulb is moved in an up-and-down, zigzag motion so as to cover eventually all the points of interest of the sound field, the camera will record as bright areas those places where the sound is strong, as gray areas those where the sound is weaker, and as black areas those where the sound is weakest. Figure 16 is a photograph, taken with this apparatus, of the sound field near the mouth of a horn loudspeaker (only the mouth of the horn is visible in the photo). In the photo we notice that the sound is loudest along the axis of the horn; the horn has "directed" the sound—that is, has made it louder in a given direction.

From Figure 16 we are justified in concluding that the technique described can be quite useful in exploring the directional properties of various acoustic devices; we shall discuss these possibilities later on. Let us not deviate, however, from our original course, which was to convince ourselves that sound is a wave phenomenon. So far we have devised a portrayal technique which permits us to depict the

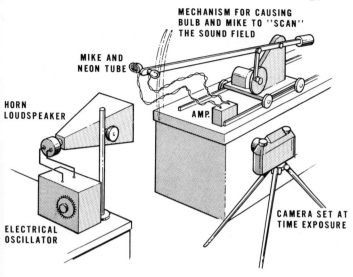

FIG. 15. A single microphone-light combination "scanning" an area of interest could record on film the space pattern of sound intensity generated by a horn loudspeaker.

variations in loudness of the sound field. We have reached the stage where we were when we had a fixed card and the pencil-equipped bobbers in the water wave experiment. In that situation the size of the mark on the card indicated the amplitude of the water wave disturbance, but the wave nature of the water wave was not yet evident. Our next step then is to duplicate, for sound waves, the moving card technique we employed for portraying the wave outline of water waves.

We recall that the motion of the card was governed by (in fact, was identical to) the motion of the wave-generating mechanism. For the sound waves we must again, somehow, make use of the

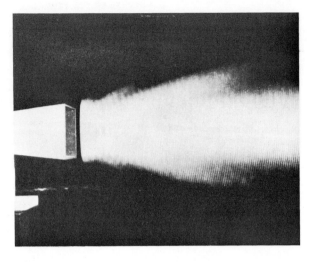

Fig. 16. The pattern of sound intensity caused by the pyramidal horn loudspeaker on the left can be portrayed visually with the apparatus of Fig. 15. The horn has a six-inch-square aperture; the sound waves being radiated have a frequency of 9000 cycles per second.

mechanism that creates the sound. Because we are using a loudspeaker for our source, we must supply it with an electrical signal, and this signal will be an electrical counterpart of the sound generated by the speaker. Can we generate an electrical input signal that will be simple and undulatory, corresponding to the up-and-down motion of the plunger of our water wave experiment? The rotation of the wheel and the connecting rod caused the plunger to follow an up-and-down motion which created the undulating water waves. In the electrical case we employ a to-and-fro *electrical* current, as generated by an electrical "oscillator" or "tone generator." This oscillation causes the loudspeaker diaphragm to move back and forth, thereby creating *sound* waves.

We have access to a sound-generating mechanism, but how do we use it? In the water wave experiment the motion of the card caused the bobbers moving in exact synchronism with the card to leave very small marks, while the marks of the bobbers that moved oppositely were quite large. If the undulating electrical signal we are delivering to the loudspeaker is combined with the electrical signal being picked up by the microphone, there should be comparable variations in the light-bulb current. In the water wave pattern there were regions of cancellation and regions of addition of wave amplitudes. If sound is a wave phenomenon, there must be, at any instant in time, regions in a sound field where the sound pressure is above normal (positive) and other regions where it is below normal (negative). At that same instant our electrical signal at the oscillator also will have a certain value—we will suppose it to be above normal (positive).

Figure 17 shows what happens when two sine waves are combined. As the two come together (the waves are then said to be in phase) *constructive interference* results, and the combined signal is larger than either one. But when the two move oppositely

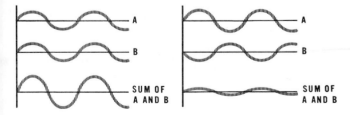

FIG. 17 Two waves of the same wavelength add (at the left) if they are phased alike and subtract (at the right) if they are out of phase.

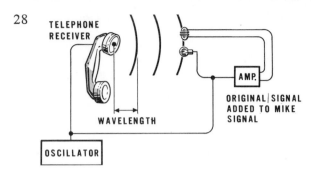

TELEPHONE
RECEIVER

AMP.

ORIGINAL | SIGNAL
ADDED TO MIKE
SIGNAL

WAVELENGTH

OSCILLATOR

FIG. 18. Combining the mike signal with the original signal results in wave addition or wave subtraction, depending upon the position of the microphone relative to the sound source.

FIG. 19. When the wave addition and subtraction technique of FIG. 18 is employed, the actual wave fronts of sound waves can be portrayed. At a frequency of 4000 cycles a telephone receiver is relatively non-directional and the sound waves spread out in all directions.

(they are then said to be out of phase) *destructive interference* occurs, and the combined signal is smaller than either one. Obviously constructive or destructive interference will happen to the microphone signal when combined with the generator signal. At points in space that are one, two, three, etc., wavelengths distant from the loudspeaker, the signals will add and the light bulb will be bright, but at the half-wavelength points the signals will subtract and the light bulb will be dim. Figure 18 sketches the circuit of the technique we have discussed. Figure 19 is a photograph of a sound wave radiating from a telephone receiver. The similarity to water waves is evident in the circular spreading of the sound waves.

Seeing Electromagnetic Waves

Exactly the same method has proved feasible for portraying electromagnetic waves. As we pointed out earlier, both light and radio waves are electromagnetic in nature, but the techniques for generating light waves *coherently* (that is, as continuous sine waves similar to the water waves and sound waves) are quite new and rather involved.* We will find it convenient to use radio waves for our experiment.

Figure 20 shows how the amplitude pattern of electromagnetic waves can be portrayed, again using a camera as a recording medium. The waves are the very short radio waves called microwaves, generated by a radio tube called a Klystron, which is

---

* The LASER, which stands for Light Amplification by Stimulated Emission of Radiation, is a device for generating highly coherent light waves.

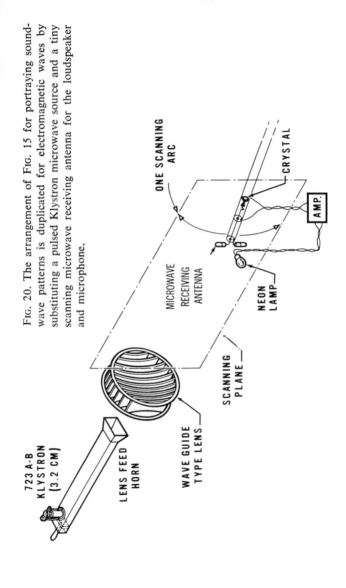

FIG. 20. The arrangement of FIG. 15 for portraying sound-wave patterns is duplicated for electromagnetic waves by substituting a pulsed Klystron microwave source and a tiny scanning microwave receiving antenna for the loudspeaker and microphone.

ONE SCANNING ARC

CRYSTAL

AMP.

MICROWAVE RECEIVING ANTENNA

NEON LAMP

SCANNING PLANE

WAVE GUIDE TYPE LENS

LENS FEED HORN

723 A-B KLYSTRON (3.2 CM)

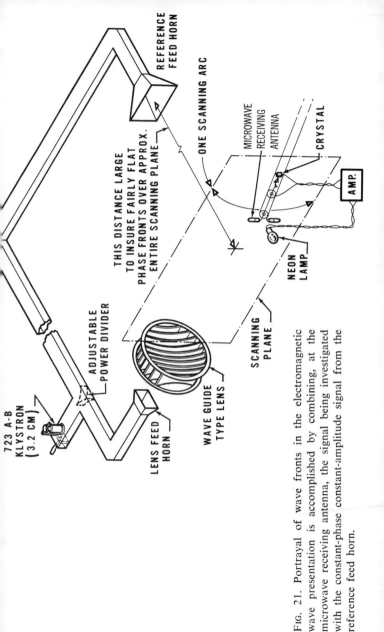

FIG. 21. Portrayal of wave fronts in the electromagnetic wave presentation is accomplished by combining, at the microwave receiving antenna, the signal being investigated with the constant-phase constant-amplitude signal from the reference feed horn.

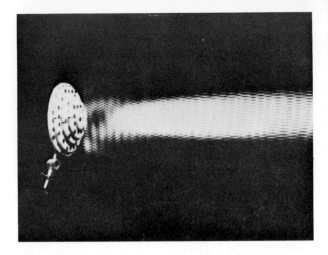

FIG. 22. A specially designed microwave lens concentrates electromagnetic wave energy (arriving from the left) into a narrow pencil-like beam. The frequency employed is 9,100,-000,000 cycles per second. This photo was taken with the arrangement of apparatus illustrated in FIG. 20.

turned on and off at a rapid rate (60 times a second). They are conducted along a rectangular metal tube called a "wave guide" to a small horn from which they issue. A rather strange-looking "lens" is shown in the figure. Its ability to focus or "beam" the microwaves is the subject we will try to investigate while, at the same time, we are exploring the wave nature of electromagnetic radiation.

The detecting and measuring device we now employ is a tiny radio antenna consisting of two rods each ¼ wavelength long.† Connected across the two halves of the antenna is a crystal rectifier (crystal detector). This device *rectifies* an undulating sig-

---

† Such antennas are often used for television; for this application each ¼ wavelength is several feet long. Note that here the microwaves are vertically polarized.

nal, that is, it converts it into a steady one. The 9,100,000,000 variations per second in the microwave signal are eliminated and only the 60-cycle "on-off" variations in the generated signal remain. These 60-cycle variations, amplified by the same amplifier used in the sound wave experiment, cause the neon bulb to light. As in our acoustic experiment with the horn, the intensity or strength of the microwave field determines the brightness of the neon lamp. The beam created by another strange "lens" is shown in Figure 22. The wave-guide feed is not visible in the picture, but the bright pencil beam is the result of the focusing action of the microwave lens.

The arrangement of Figure 20 examines only the amplitude pattern of the electromagnetic field, just as our first bobber and microphone techniques portrayed only the wave amplitude of the pond and the sound field. To picture the actual wave pattern we again make use of a wave-generating mechanism, here the Klystron tube. Fig. 21 shows how the generating signal can be combined with the focused signals in the microwave field to create the additions and subtractions needed to form a wave pattern. A U-shaped section of wave guide takes part of the microwave energy from the Klystron and radiates it from a second horn radiator, which is aimed at the microwave field of interest. The waves emerge from this second horn in the same spherical (circular) pattern of water waves or sound waves, but if this horn is placed quite far back the circles become very large by the time they reach the microwave receiver antenna. Now a short arc of a very large circle is almost a straight line and, similarly, a small surface of a large sphere is almost a plane surface. Hence, over the plane that the receiving antenna scans, the wave condition of the second horn waves (such as a crest or a trough) will be practically uniform. The waves emerging from the first horn (and its lens) move out at right angles to those of the second horn and, accordingly, additions and subtractions will occur between these two sets of waves. At the instant when the second horn is producing a wave crest at the scanning plane, *additions* will occur at all of the wave *crests* of the first horn waves and *subtractions* will occur at the wave *troughs*. This *combined* pattern in the scanning plane remains constant at all times—that is, even as both sets of waves progress outward. Thus, when the second horn produces a wave *trough* over the entire scanning plane, the first horn waves will have

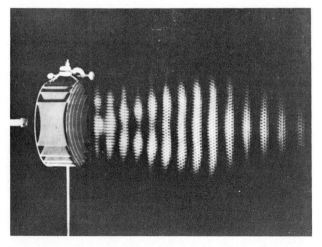

Fig. 23. With the arrangement of Fig. 21 the wave fronts present in a focused electromagnetic beam can be portrayed. The wave guide at the far left is placed at the focal point of the microwave lens, and the wave fronts of the directed energy appear in the center of the picture.

moved out so that their troughs and crests will have changed places, and the original additive pattern still remains. Scanning this spatially fixed pattern with the receiving antenna and the neon lamp thus portrays visually the progressive wave pattern of the microwaves issuing from horn number one and its associated lens. The arrangement of Figure 21 was used to obtain Figure 23, which shows a pattern of microwaves focused by a metallic lens. The waveguide feed for the lens is shown at the left. The frequency of the microwaves (9,100,000,000 cycles per second) corresponds to a wavelength of 1.3 inches, which is the spacing between successive waves shown in the photograph. We note in this photograph that the wave fronts are not circular as in Figure 19; rather, they are straight (i.e., sections of planes). This is characteristic of wave energy that is *directed,* as against wave energy that is not but spreads out in all directions as in Figure 19.

Chapter III

WAVE PROPAGATION

Much can be learned about waves from an examination of their "wave front" patterns. We have seen (page 33) that when wave energy spreads in many directions, the wave fronts are circular (as on the pond) or spherical (as the sound from the telephone receiver).* When the wave energy is directed, the wave fronts are flat (Figure 23). How do waves propagate in the regions of "shadow"? This process is called diffraction; waves are said to diffract "around" an obstacle.

Diffraction

Webster defines diffraction thusly: "A modification which light undergoes, as in passing by the edges of opaque bodies or through narrow slits, in which the rays appear to be deflected, producing fringes of parallel light and dark or colored bands; also the analogous phenomenon in the case of sound, electricity, etc." From this definition we see that there are several aspects of diffraction. We shall consider these in turn.

When waves pass the edges of opaque bodies, some energy is deflected (diffracted) into the shadow region. This phenomenon is illustrated in

---

* The circular wave fronts of Figure 19 are actually cross sections of the spherical wave fronts of the sound waves.

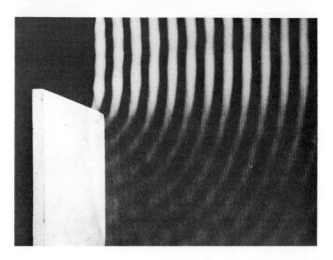

FIG. 24. Plane sound waves arriving from the left proceed unhindered at the top of the photo. In the shadow region below circular wave fronts are evident, caused by diffraction at the edge of the shadowing object.

Figure 24, taken by the method described in the last chapter. In this photograph, sound waves are arriving from the left, and the wooden board acts as a shadowing object. In the region above the board the waves continue on unimpeded toward the right, but since the waves cannot penetrate the board (it is "opaque" to the sound waves), the lower right of the photo is a "shadow" region. The upper edge of the board constitutes an interfering object (often referred to as a knife-edge), which acts as a "new" source of sound energy. The waves in the shadow region thus appear to originate from this knife-edge. The wave fronts there are circular (cylindrical) with their centers located at the knife-edge.

Suppose now we use a disk instead of a knife-edge for the opaque object. The energy will be deflected from all points of the perimeter of the disk,

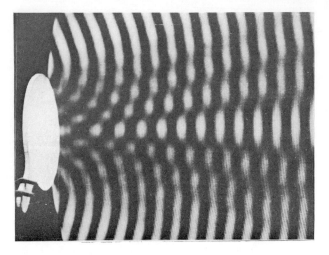

Fig. 25. Sound waves diffracted around a circular disk combine in the shadow region and produce a central beam of parallel wave fronts.

and a more complicated wave pattern will exist in the cylindrical shadow region cast by this disk. This situation is shown in Figure 25. Sound waves again are arriving from the left, and in the upper and lower parts of the photo the waves proceed unhindered. In the shadow region two sets of circular wave fronts are seen, one having the top edge as common center and the other having the lower edge as center. These wave fronts "interfere" with one another; that is, their energies add and subtract. Out of this complicated mixture we see emerging along the axis a narrow wave pattern that looks much like the pattern of the unimpeded waves at the top and bottom of the photo and that proceeds in the same direction. The combination of the "new" wave sources on the circular edge of the disk has produced a concentration of energy along the axis.

Lord Rayleigh first predicted and observed this

Fig. 26. When the amplitude pattern in the shadow of a disk is examined, the bright central lobe is clearly evident.

effect in light waves. Using a penny as his opaque object and a shaft of sunlight as his source of light waves, he noticed the presence of a bright spot in the center of the circular shadow of the penny. Figure 26 is a repeat of Figure 25, using the same source and circular object. This time, however, the phase signal has been removed. Only the amplitude pattern of the sound waves behind the disk is shown now, and the existence of Rayleigh's "bright spot" is clearly demonstrated.

Unusual diffraction effects are created when light passes through slits in an opaque screen. As Webster states, "fringes" and "dark or colored bands" of light then occur. To see how this comes about, we can duplicate the slits by using two non-directional sound sources and examine, through our visual portrayal methods, the pattern created by the two sound sources. Figure 27 shows the pattern for two

Fig. 27. Two separated sound sources act like two optical slits in creating a diffraction pattern by constructive and destructive interference.

9000-cycle-per-second sound wave sources separated by 3 wavelengths ($\lambda=1.51''$). If the two sources are in phase, the combination of the two uniform wave fields results in wave addition at points in space that are equidistant from the two radiating points. That this is so we can see in the bright area running from left to right along the central line. At points in space differing in their distance from the two sources by one-half wavelength, wave cancellation or destructive interference results. One of the two waves has positive pressure where the other has negative pressure, and vice versa. This effect was explained in Chapter II in connection with Figure 16. This interfering effect produces the black areas in Figure 27 immediately above and below the central bright area. The next bright areas occur in areas where the distances from the two sources differ by a full wavelength. The waves are again in phase, and the positive pressures add and the negative pressures also add. In areas where the distances differ by any *integral* number of wavelengths, wave addition (constructive interference) always results. Thus all the bright areas in Figure 27 (called *fringes* in optics and *lobes* in sound and radio) are such additive or constructive interference regions. Finally, we note that if the distances differ by any odd number of half wavelengths (½, ³⁄₂, etc.) we again find destructive interference. The second set of two black valleys at the upper and lower parts of Figure 27 are areas whose distances differ by 3 half wavelengths.

If the waves portrayed in Figure 27 were light waves and the radiators were long slits perpendicular to the paper, a screen placed a short distance away would display the series of bright and dark bands called "fringes" in optics. We noted that Webster says "colored" bands. Since the dark areas in Figure 27 are regions whose distances to the two sources differ by an odd number of half wavelengths, waves with longer or shorter wavelengths (frequencies) than the waves used to obtain Figure 27 would generate somewhat different space patterns (diffraction patterns). A wave of one frequency could generate a bright area on the screen exactly where another frequency would produce a dark area. Since white light is made up of many frequencies (colors), a diffraction pattern of white light actually would consist of the various diffraction patterns, each one produced by each of the various colors. These various patterns would not be in registry on the screen, one on top of another, to recompose white light. Instead, colored "fringes" would result.

42

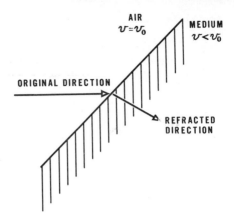

Fig. 28. When wave energy leaves one medium and enters another on the oblique, the ray direction is deflected if the velocities of propagation in the two media differ.

Refraction

The velocity of propagation of waves is not the same for all substances. Thus light waves travel faster in air than they do in water or glass. When waves leave one medium (in which they travel at one speed) and enter another (in which they travel at another speed), an important phenomenon occurs; their direction of travel is deflected. This process, called refraction, can be visualized in two ways. Figure 28 employs ray concepts to indicate how a "ray" of light is deflected when it enters the new medium. Figure 29, on the other hand, utilizes the wave-front picture to show how the waves themselves are affected when they enter the lower velocity medium. The motion of the wave fronts can be compared to the movement of rows of marching soldiers crossing a boundary at an angle into a field (perhaps a plowed one) where they have to slow their pace. The change in velocity brings about a change in direction. After the first soldiers cross the boundary and begin to march more slowly, the others of the row follow suit in succession, and when the entire row has crossed, the column's direction of travel has changed. It is apparent that the equation (frequency times wavelength equals velocity) is involved in the situation of Figure 29. The *frequency* of a wave is a constant; hence a change in wave velocity must be accompanied by a corresponding change in wavelength. This change is indicated in Figure 29 in the smaller separation of the parallel lines (rows) within the medium.

The ratio of the velocities in the two media provides a measure of the extent of the ray-bending, or refraction. This ratio is called the index of refraction. The letter *n* is assigned to this quantity, and the

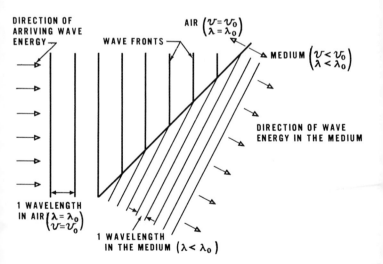

Fig. 29. Wave energy entering a low-velocity medium experiences a shortening of its wavelength; the direction of propagation is altered accordingly.

equation expressing the index of refraction of a particular substance is $n = v_0/v$ where v_0 is the free space velocity and v the velocity in the medium. Optically refractive substances such as water, glass, and diamond all have refractive indices exceeding unity; that is, the wave velocity for light waves in these media is less than the velocity of light in free space.

Prisms

In Figures 28 and 29 we considered what occurred at the interface between air and a refractive medium (lower wave velocity). Let us now see what happens when wave energy first enters and then later *emerges* from a refracting substance. Figure 30 shows a cross section of a glass optical prism; a light ray is shown entering the left side and emerging at the right. The ray is bent, or refracted, in entering the prism and it is again refracted upon leaving the prism. A wave-front picture of this phenomenon in the style of Figure 29 would give the emerging ray (direction of wave propagation) the same direction.

Prisms often are used to separate the different wavelengths present in a composite electromagnetic wave. This separation (or decomposition) is possible because many optical materials have refractive indices that vary with the wavelength or frequency of electromagnetic waves. As shown in Figure 30, a glass prism, which has a slightly different index of refraction for each of the various colors making up white light, deflects the red rays less than the blue rays. The prism thus causes the various colors of the spectrum to be separated. A material whose refractive index is frequency-de-

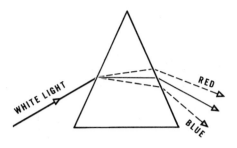

Fig. 30. The wave velocity of red light entering a glass prism is not reduced as much as is the velocity of blue light.

pendent is called *dispersive*. A prism of such material is said to exhibit *dispersion*.

The deflection of wave direction by a prism can be exhibited for sound waves also. Figure 31 portrays a situation where sound is first radiated from a small conical horn loudspeaker, then focused into a beam by a special acoustic lens† and passed through an acoustic prism. Had the prism not been in place, the beam would have been pointed in a horizontal direction; the prism has deflected the beam downward.

The acoustic prism of Figure 31 also exhibits dispersion for sound waves. Figure 32 indicates the amount of beam deflection for sound waves of different frequencies. Just as a glass prism separates the different electromagnetic frequencies constituting white light, so the acoustic prism can separate the different frequency components of a sound wave consisting of several tones of different frequency, or pitch.

It so happens that the prism shown in Figure 31 is effective for both sound waves and electromagnetic waves in the microwave frequency range. (We

† This type of lens is described in further detail in Chapter VII.

FIG. 31. The focused beam of sound waves formed by an acoustic lens is deflected downward by an acoustic prism.

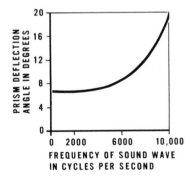

FIG. 32. The prism of FIG. 31 possesses an index of refraction for sound waves which is dependent upon the frequency of the waves.

shall discuss the reason for this in a later chapter.) Furthermore, if the wavelengths of the microwaves and sound waves are the same, they are both deflected the same amount. For this particular prism a rather unusual situation exists; the variation of refractive index with *wavelength* is the same for the two types of waves.

Wave Focusing

Figure 31 showed the prism with its thick end down; the waves were deflected downward. Had the thick end of the prism been up, the beam would have been deflected upward. Imagine now (Figure 31) a second prism placed below the first one with the thick ends of both prisms in juxtaposition. Imagine also a second source of wave energy to the left of the lower prism. There would then be two beams, the original one deflected downward from the upper prism and a second one deflected upward from the new, lower, prism. At the point where the two deflected beams crossed, a concentration of energy would exist.

Such a concentration of wave energy is called *focusing*. The region of energy concentration is called the *focal point*. Together, the two triangular prisms have a cross section that approximates the cross section of a focusing lens such as a reading glass. Both are thin at the top edge, thick in the center, and thin again at the lower edge.

Lenses

The two prisms just discussed focus or concentrate energy in one dimension only—the vertical plane. Focusing in both the horizontal and vertical

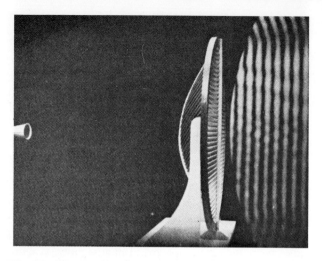

FIG. 33. An acoustic lens converts into plane waves the circular wave fronts of sound waves issuing from a horn placed at the focal point of the lens.

planes is accomplished with a refracting structure that is circular in outline, thin around its entire perimeter and thick in the center. This circular lens concentrates energy at a focal point lying on its axis. Its refractive properties cause a redirection of energy propagation which results in focusing.

In Figure 33 sound waves are shown being acted upon by such a circular lens (thin at the edge and thick at the center). The horn from which the sound waves originate is portrayed at the left, and the wave field is only sampled to the right of the lens. In this region the straight lines show that the circular wave fronts radiating from the horn (they are not shown in the figure) have been converted to plane wave fronts after passing through the lens.

Since wave processes are *reciprocal*—that is, the same phenomena occur whether the wave energy is traveling in one direction or the other—energy from

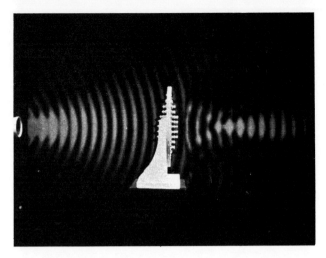

Fig. 34. Circularly diverging sound waves issuing from the horn at the left are converted, by the acoustic lens, into circularly converging waves at the right.

some distant source can be considered as arriving *from the right* in Figure 33; the lens then causes the energy falling upon its right-hand surface to be focused in the region where the feed horn is placed. The feed horn, being at the focal point of the lens, receives a maximum amount of energy.

In the first example of Figure 33 (energy transmitted from the left) the maximum beaming effect is obtained when the source of wave energy (the small horn) is placed at the focal point; conversely, in the second example (energy received from right) the horn is again placed at the point where maximum focusing of received energy occurs —that is, at the focal point.

A lens can be employed also to cause spreading energy to concentrate again into a second focal area. The lens then has two focal points. Figure 34 shows this situation with the wave field sampled and portrayed on both sides of the lens. The energy is seen spreading out from the horn at the left; the circular lines now visible in this figure (they were not visible in Figure 33) are evidence of the circular spreading waves. After the waves pass through the lens the wave fronts become concave inward, and a concentration of wave energy is seen to the right of the lens. This particular lens is called *double convex* because both its front and back surfaces are curved. The lens in Figure 33 is called plano-convex because one surface is plane and the other is curved (convex).

Chapter IV

WAVE RADIATION

By what process is wave propagation initiated? How do acoustic and electromagnetic sources create different radiation patterns? If we examine some of the different effects that can be produced by varying the designs of radiators, perhaps we can find answers, or partial answers, to these questions.

Horns

In the mists of antiquity some caveman or tree dweller discovered that his bellowing to his mate carried farther when he cupped his hands around his mouth. Later, he or an inventive descendant magnified the effect by shouting or blowing through a hollow animal horn or a piece of bark wrapped in the conical shape of a megaphone. Man had learned to modify sound radiation. An acoustic horn, as we saw in Figure 16, has a radiation pattern that causes the energy to be concentrated in the direction in which the horn is aimed. On the other hand, the acoustic radiation pattern of a telephone receiver (Figure 19) shows no such concentration or directional tendency. Why should the horn have this pronounced directional effect?

In Figure 35 the circular wave fronts of a non-directional sound source are portrayed. The energy radiates in all directions. Since the circles (which

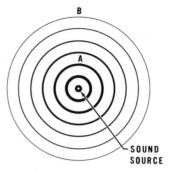

FIG. 35. Sound waves from a non-directional sound source move out in all directions and the energy at a point in each successive ring becomes smaller. Because of this dissipation of energy the sound at A is louder than at B. The weight of line in a circle suggests the relative energy at that distance from source.

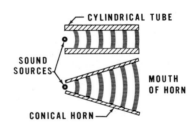

FIG. 36. Wave energy, such as sound, propagating in a cylindrical tube does not spread out; the intensity or loudness remains fairly constant. The situation is somewhat similar in a conical tube.

really are sections of spheres) grow larger and the energy stays constant, the sound energy passing through any given area will become less as the distance from the sound source increases. We have indicated this relationship by showing a decreasing thickness of the circular lines representing the wave fronts as the circles become larger. A person listening at point A would find himself in a stronger or more intense sound field than a person at point B.

In Figure 36 we have caused the sound energy to be confined, first in a cylindrical tube, then in a conical horn. Within the tube there is no divergence of energy and the intensity of sound remains fairly constant all along the tube (indicated by the constant thickness of the wave fronts). Within the horn there is some divergence but because all the energy is confined within the horn, the intensity at its mouth remains quite high. In addition, the wave fronts at the mouth of the horn are rather flat, and since energy propagates along a line perpendicular to the wave fronts, we can expect a concentration of sound energy in the direction in which the horn is pointed.

How flat must the wave fronts be for the best directional effect? Theory and measurement show that when phase curvature is so small that only ⅛ of a wavelength curvature exists over the entire aperture (as in Figure 37), the effectiveness of the radiation can hardly be distinguished from the ideally flat-phase situation. Accordingly, the criterion often used for a microwave radiator is that the phase must be flat to within $\pm 1/16$ of a wavelength.

If they are to produce phase fronts flat to $\pm 1/16$ of a wavelength, large-aperture horns become exceedingly long. The geometry is shown in Figure 38 for two horns of different aperture. The horn, having an aperture of only 2 wavelengths, must be 4 wavelengths long to satisfy the ⅛-wavelength curvature requirement, whereas a horn of 5 wavelengths' aperture must be 25 wavelengths long. A horn with an aperture of 20 wavelengths would have to be 400 wavelengths long!

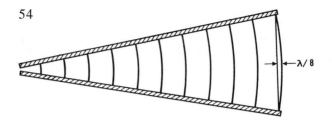

FIG. 37. When the curvature of the wave fronts issuing from a horn is very small, a strong directional property is inherent in the radiated energy. When the phase difference is as indicated, only an eighth of a wavelength, the directivity is insignificantly different from a truly flat wave front.

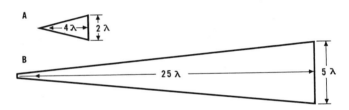

FIG. 38. To hold the wave front curvature to one eighth of a wavelength, the required horn length is set by the aperture size in wavelengths. A small-aperture horn (at A) can be short, but a large-aperture horn (at B) must be long.

Lenses

Now, if flat wave fronts at the aperture are required for high efficiency in concentrating wave energy in a given direction, and if large apertures require very long horns, practicality would seem to demand a technique of modification. Figure 33 shows that circular wave fronts can be made plane by the use of a lens. Further, Figure 33 portrays flat wave fronts emanating from a lens whose aperture is quite large. The lens is 30 inches in diameter, and, since the wavelengths used in the photo are approximately 1.5 inches, the lens aperture is 20 wavelengths. We thus see that the lens has permitted an appreciable shortening of the length dimension compared to a normal horn. The feed for the lens of Figure 34 (at the left of the photo) was placed only 30 inches behind the rear lens surface. Compare this distance with 400 wavelengths, which for a wavelength of 1.5 inches would be fifty feet!

In some microwave applications a lens is placed in the mouth of the horn. The horn length can then be made short without losing the advantages of the horn. One such advantage (in the case of microwave radio-beam transmission) is the shielding effect the horn provides. Radio waves do not penetrate conducting sheets of metal, and the microwave horns thus confine the energy.

In our brief discussion of glass lenses in Chapter III we observed that the cross section of a lens, like two juxtaposed prisms, is thick in the center and thin at the edge. We can ascertain the desired profile of a lens more explicitly from Figure 39. We assume that energy is emerging at the focal point, and we want a ray with a part of its path in the refracting material of the lens to be equal in "phase length" to a ray not affected by the lens. That is to say, we want the time taken for wave energy to the front face of the lens to be the same for all parts of the lens. To meet these conditions the contour of the lens must be a hyperbola. For the profile to be hyperbolic in all planes, the left-hand surface of the lens will be a hyperboloid of revolution. In practice, however, most optical lenses have spherical surfaces, hyperboloidal surfaces being hard to grind.

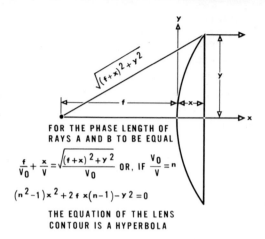

FOR THE PHASE LENGTH OF
RAYS A AND B TO BE EQUAL

$$\frac{f}{V_0} + \frac{x}{V} = \frac{\sqrt{(f+x)^2 + y^2}}{V_0} \quad \text{OR, IF} \quad \frac{V_0}{V} = n$$

$$(n^2 - 1)x^2 + 2fx(n-1) - y^2 = 0$$

THE EQUATION OF THE LENS
CONTOUR IS A HYPERBOLA

FIG. 39. For the radiated wave fronts from a lens to be flat, the times of travel of all rays from the focal point to the flat front surface of the lens must be alike. The lower velocity of propagation within the lens accomplishes this if the lens is made thick at its center.

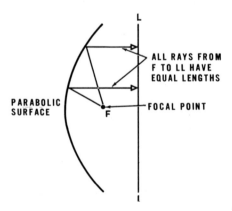

FIG. 40. A curved reflector also can create the situation where the times of travel of all rays from a focal point to a plane are alike.

Parabolic Reflectors

Another form of radiator that produces flat wave fronts in small space is the focusing reflector. We want energy originating at the focal point F in Figure 40 to arrive at the line LL with flat wave fronts after reflection from the curved surface. From the definition of a parabola, all lines (rays) that originate at F will, after reflection, return perpendicular to LL and will have the same length, *if* the curve is a parabola. Accordingly, a reflector that is paraboloid of revolution will effect focusing in all planes.

Parabolic reflectors are used in searchlight mirrors, radar antennas, and in some acoustical microphones designed for listening to distant sounds. One quite useful microwave radiator is the combination of a horn and a section of a parabolic reflector. A photo of such an antenna is shown in Figure 41; its method of operation is depicted in the sketch of Figure 42. The apex of the horn is placed at the focal point of a parabolic surface and only the part of the parabolic surface that intersects the pyramidal horn is used. The waves emerging at the right have flat phase fronts because of the action of the paraboloidal reflector section. This type of radiator has the same shielding advantages that a horn radiator or horn-lens combination possesses.

Arrays

From the horn, the lens, and the parabolic reflector we have sought to obtain a radiated wave front having flat phase. Still another method of achieving this goal is to use a large number of individual radiators, all energized in phase. This method is illustrated in Figure 43, where many

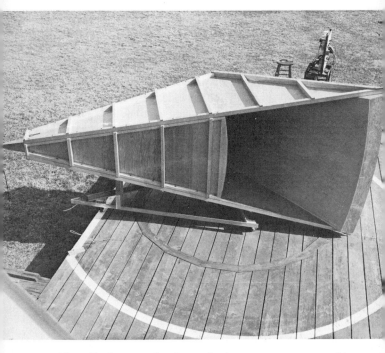

FIG. 41. One popular form of microwave antenna combines a horn with a parabolic reflecting surface whose focal point is at the throat of the horn.

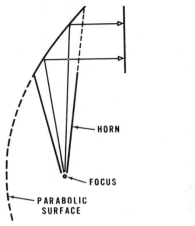

FIG. 42. Part of a parabolic reflector can be used in conjunction with a horn to produce flat wave fronts. By guiding the energy to the reflector, the horn provides an advantageous shielding effect.

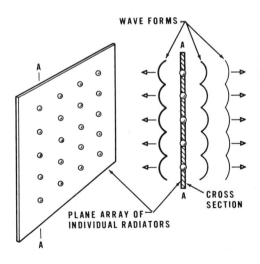

FIG. 43. An array of individual radiators, themselves nondirectional, becomes a directional radiator of plane wave fronts if the elements radiate in phase.

small sound sources of the type used in Figure 27 are connected to make the phases of all radiated signals alike. Although the individual radiators are non-directional, when they are placed in a plane their outputs combine to create two plane waves moving in opposite directions. If, as shown in Figure 44, a reflecting plate is placed the proper distance behind the plane of the radiators, the wave moving in one direction will be reflected and will add to the wave moving in the opposite direction. An array constitutes a directional source of very small axial dimensions.

The spacing of the individual radiators is important. If we place the radiators far apart (as in Figure 27), objectionable side lobes are produced. Theory shows that if the radiators are spaced a half wavelength apart, phase addition can occur only in the direction perpendicular to the line joining the two radiators. Objectionable side lobes are eliminated.

Radiation perpendicular to the plane of the radiators is called "broadside radiation." In most broadside arrays the individual radiators are spaced a half wavelength apart.

End-fire Arrays

Figure 45 shows a series of radiators energized by a single source but with a "delay" incorporated between the individual radiating elements. If the individual delays are made equal to the time of radiated wave travel from one element to the next, the radiated waves will add in phase along the line joining the radiating elements. Such arrays are called "end-fire" arrays: they radiate off the end of the linear structure making up the array. The array directs wave energy as a hose directs water.

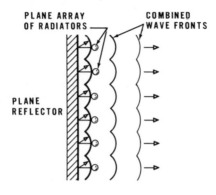

FIG. 44. A reflector plate placed behind the array of FIG. 32 causes it to radiate in one direction only.

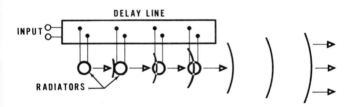

FIG. 45. An end-fire array results when radiators are placed in a row and energized, not in phase, but in such a way that proper phase addition occurs in a given direction. In the illustration, this direction is to the right.

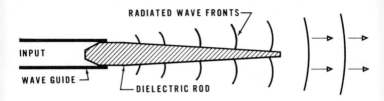

Fig. 46. A tapered dielectric rod which not only guides electromagnetic energy but also radiates it gradually, constitutes a useful end-fire radiator.

Individual radiators can be energized by a transmission line (Figure 45) or the transmission line can be used as its own radiator. Figure 46 shows a microwave end-fire radiator used in some early radar equipment. Microwave energy arriving from the left is confined within a hollow conducting tube which is called a wave guide (we shall discuss these in more detail in the next chapter). Into the end of the tube there is inserted an insulating (non-conducting or "dielectric") rod. Because the dielectric rod is usually made of the translucent plastic called polystyrene, it is often called a "polyrod." The waves continue to advance into the rod, but at the point where the conducting wave guide ends, a small amount of wave energy begins to "leak" out. The rod is tapered in its cross-sectional area, and, as the waves progress, more and more energy continues to be radiated from it over its entire length. Because the energy radiating from successive parts of the dielectric rod is traveling at a velocity very close to the velocity of light in free space, the dielectric rod acts like the end-fire radiator we have described. Good directional patterns are achieved in the direction in which the dielectric rod is pointed.

Chapter V

WAVE GUIDES

In the years just prior to and during World War II, a new method of transmitting electromagnetic energy was developed. This method, which evolved mainly from the work of research groups at the Massachusetts Institute of Technology and the Bell Telephone Laboratories, used hollow tubes called *wave guides* to conduct the energy and seemed to upset the popular ideas about the transport of electricity.

To appreciate how radical a break with common practice this new development was, we might reflect for a moment on our own experience with electrical theory. Most of us were introduced to the concept of electric "current" in discussions and demonstrations of direct current, which "flows" when a battery is hooked up to a flashlight bulb or some other device. We saw that two wires were needed to deliver energy to the bulb or motor; we called them the "direct" and "return" leads. Current could flow to the device over the direct lead and back to the battery over the return lead.

When we progressed to alternating current we learned that things are only a little different. A toy electric train transformer circuit, which uses alternating electric current, cannot be said to have a return lead since both leads, because of the "back-and-forth" nature of the flow, act first as current "suppliers" and then as current "returners." Nevertheless, such circuits still have two leads. So does a telephone circuit carrying currents which alternate back and forth at several thousands of times per second. Even the extremely high-frequency transmission circuit, the coaxial cable, which carries currents with frequencies of millions of cycles per second, possesses, in addition to one central conductor, an outer cylindrical conducting shell that can be looked upon as constituting the second "wire" of the circuit.

Accordingly, when the wave-guide developers announced the transporting of electrical energy over a single conductor, a hollow metal tube, obvious questions were asked. Where is the return circuit? If the current travels out in the tubular conductor, how does it get back? Of course when wave guides were described to physicists experienced in optical matters, no such consternation resulted. They recognized that radio waves and light waves, both electromagnetic, would behave alike, and the idea of passing light waves down a tube with mirrorlike walls seemed not at all radical. For our purposes, we shall think of the wave guide not as a conductor of electricity, but as a confining structure for propagating electromagnetic waves. All we have to bear in mind is that the wavelengths of the radio waves involved are so short that the waves confined by the guide behave like light waves.

Rectangular Wave Guides

When radio waves are propagating within the enclosed conducting structure of a wave guide, they can exhibit various energy distributions. Thus the

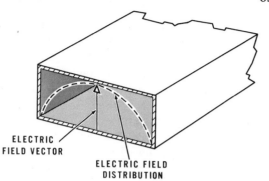

ELECTRIC FIELD VECTOR

ELECTRIC FIELD DISTRIBUTION

FIG. 47. The electric field in a rectangular wave guide is strong in the center and zero at the edges.

energy or the intensity of the electromagnetic field can be strong at the center and weak at the walls, or it can be strong in several areas and weak in others. The number of different distributions possible depends upon the size of the structure in relation to the wavelength of the waves. The simplest of such energy configurations is called the "dominant" configuration, or more usually, the *dominant* transmission mode. It is shown in Figure 47 for a rectangular wave guide. The metal side walls "short-circuit" the electric field, and it falls to zero there. Other energy distributions or configurations that can occur are called *higher order modes*. When the wave-guide width is less than a wavelength and the height less than a half wavelength, all these higher-order modes are prevented from propagating; only the fundamental or dominant configuration is then possible. Since the dominant mode is by far the most important mode in the practical application of wave guides, we shall not discuss further the higher-order modes. One additional requirement for supporting a wave propagating in the dominant mode is that the width dimension of the guide must exceed a half wavelength. Wave-guide runs need not be straight, and the waves can be conducted around corners, along spiral paths, etc. Wave-guide transmission systems now in common use can pass radio frequencies ranging from about 1000 million to 70,000 million cycles per second.

Wave guides permit the transmission of radio waves over moderate distances with relatively low losses. Also, the conducting tube acts as a very effective shield and prevents interaction between very high energy signals propagating in one wave guide and low amplitude signals in another wave guide nearby. The rectangular shape of the guide causes the polarization of the wave to be maintained relative to the guide orientation—that is, the wave polarization remains perpendicular to the large wall of the guide even though the wave guide is given a twist. In a circular wave guide (round wave guide) there is no such restraint on the wave polarization. In circular guides, therefore, the wave polarization will tend to rotate as the wave proceeds down the guide unless the guide is made precisely circular.

Wave Velocity

A strange thing happens to electromagnetic waves confined within a wave guide: the energy slows down and the waves speed up! When electromagnetic waves travel unhindered in free space, the velocity of propagation of energy is the same as the speed with which the crests and troughs of the waves move. But in wave guides these two velocities must be differentiated, for they are not the same. We call the velocity of propagation of the energy the *group velocity,* and the speed with which the crests and troughs of the waves themselves move the *phase velocity.*

The difference between group velocity and phase velocity is observable when a stone is thrown into a still pond. Ripples are caused which grow into ever increasing circular patterns. If we concentrate on the wave crests and troughs which make up this ever increasing ring, we see that the little wavelets themselves move outward faster than the ring does. They appear to be "born" at the interior portion of the ring, and as they become waves they move faster than the ring and then die out as they reach the outer periphery of the ring. The speed of motion of the wave crests and troughs (which move faster than the ring itself) corresponds to the phase velocity, whereas the speed of motion of the ring (the energy) corresponds to the group velocity. A quite analogous situation exists within a metallic wave guide. The speed of advance of the wave crests and troughs is higher than the speed of the advance of the electrical energy. The former, the phase velocity, exceeds the wave velocity in free space and the latter, the group velocity, is less than the free-space velocity. It happens that the product of the phase and group velocities in a wave guide is equal to the square of the free-space velocity.

In exploiting this unusual wave property within a wave guide, we are more interested in the velocity of the waves themselves than in the energy velocity. Accordingly, in the following we shall deal only with the wave or phase velocity. As we learned in Chapter I, for a fixed frequency signal the wavelength is directly proportional to the velocity. A higher wave velocity within a wave guide thus must mean a longer wavelength within the guide. The free-space wavelength is usually designated as λ_0 and the wavelength within the guide as λ_G. The "stretching" of the wavelength of a radio wave entering a wave guide is illustrated in Figure 48.

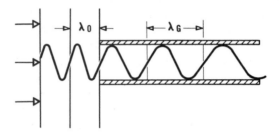

FIG. 48. Free-space radio waves arriving from the left exhibit an increase in wavelength upon entering a metallic wave guide.

The fact that phase velocity increases within a wave guide has made possible the development of unusual types of microwave lenses and other interesting wave-refracting devices. We recall that converging lenses made of glass are thick in the center and thin at the edges. This configuration is necessary because refracting materials (such as glass) exhibit a wave velocity less than the free-space velocity of light. But since wave guides, on the other hand, produce a phase velocity *greater* than the free-space velocity, a convergent lens becomes concave in shape when wave guide structures are used. Such a wave-guide lens appeared in Figure 23; we shall learn more about them in Chapter VII.

Round Wave Guides

Round wave guides have certain uses that make them attractive in specialized applications. We mentioned the problem that exists in maintaining the orientation of polarization in round wave guides. On the other hand, because they *are* round, they will support waves of any polarization, including two waves having their polarizations at right angles to one another. Thus two waves, one vertically polarized and one horizontally polarized, can be generated and detected separately, and each can be furnished with different messages or information. Since they can be transmitted independently in one round guide, two separate communication channels are available within a single wave guide.

Round guides can be used also to produce interesting polarization effects by virtue of the fact that the wave velocity of the dominant mode in a round wave guide, as in a rectangular one, depends upon the width of the guide in relation to the wavelength. If a round guide is made elliptical, waves polarized parallel to the narrow width will travel at a different velocity from that of waves polarized parallel to the wider width.

A structure formed of many elliptical tubes placed adjacent to one another like a honeycomb thus has a property possessed by certain optical materials such as tourmaline. These optical materials are called *doubly refracting* or *birefringent,* because they refract light waves of one polarization (say horizontal) differently from those of the opposite polarization (vertical). The refracting properties of optical materials are specified by their index of refraction, and we recall that this factor is related to the wave velocity within the material. Accordingly, a material that is doubly refracting exhibits a wave velocity dependent upon the direction of polarization of the waves. Since the phase velocity of microwaves passing through the elliptical-tube honeycomb also depends upon the direction of wave polarization, this structure affects microwaves just as doubly refracting materials affect light waves.

The proper thickness of doubly refracting tourmaline will rotate the polarization of linearly polarized light waves by 90°; a piece half as thick will cause circularly polarized waves to be produced. The first device is called a "half wave plate" and the second a "quarter wave plate." If we orient our elliptical wave-guide honeycomb structure at a 45° angle and assume that vertically polarized microwaves are involved, we likewise find that the wave polarization will be rotated 90° after the waves pass through the proper length of the elliptical tubing. We can see how this occurs if we regard the original vertically polarized wave as made up of two waves polarized at ±45° to the vertical. The 45° wave lining up with the narrow part of the ellipse travels with *high* phase velocity and the other 45° component travels with *low* phase velocity. At a point along the elliptical tubes the high velocity wave has advanced a half wavelength ahead of the low velocity one. If we recombine the two 45° polarizations at this point, the resultant vector is polarized at 90° to the original vector; that is, the vertically polarized wave has been transformed into a horizontally polarized wave. The elliptical tube structure is accordingly a "microwave half-wave plate." When a half-wave plate has its thickness cut in half, it becomes a quarter-wave plate, just as in optics. Similarly, linearly polarized electromagnetic waves passing through a short section can be transformed into circularly polarized waves. Because circularly polarized microwaves have proved useful in *radar* applications, let us review at this point the principles underlying microwave radar.

Radar

Radar constitutes one of the most important applications of microwave techniques. The name is coined from the words *RA*dio *D*etection *A*nd *R*anging; the technique has also been called *echolocation*. Its operation can be described as follows: A high power radio transmitter sends out in a given direction a very brief burst of microwave energy; immediately thereafter a sensitive receiver, aimed in the same direction, attempts to detect "echoes" of the microwaves as they bounce off ships or airplanes. Because microwaves can penetrate fog, clouds, etc., and because the radar works just as well at night as in the daytime, radar has proved very useful not only in military applications but also in civilian air and sea transportation.

The use of circularly polarized microwaves came about because rainstorms often reflect radar signals. The raindrops themselves reflect the microwaves and generate "echoes" which clutter up the radar screen. For certain applications, the rain echoes are not objectionable; in fact, many commercial aircraft today carry "weather radars" which permit detection of heavy rain areas in the sky and thereby warn the pilot to change course to avoid these turbulent areas. When a ground radar is being used to locate an aircraft target, however, any rain echo constitutes an interfering signal that can prevent the operator from detecting the aircraft. In this situation circularly polarized waves can be used to suppress the rain echo and permit the echo from the aircraft target to be seen. The spherical nature of raindrops causes the circularly polarized waves to be returned to the receiver with their circular polarization properties virtually unaffected. On the other hand, an irregular object such as an aircraft "depolarizes" the circularly polarized waves to a certain extent. The radar receiver is set to reject circularly polarized waves and to accept the depolarized waves; the target then becomes visible.

Dielectric Wave Guides

In Chapter IV we mentioned a microwave radiator consisting of a tapered dielectric rod inserted in a metal wave guide. You will recall that as the cross-sectional dimension is reduced, more and more energy radiates from the rod. Suppose that instead of reducing the cross section, we continued the rod at full thickness to great lengths? We would discover that practically no energy is radiated and that the dielectric rod acts as a wave "guide" or transmission line. This guiding effect of a dielectric rod is a consequence of the lower wave velocity in the rod. As seen in Figure 49, the lower velocity causes a tilting of the wave fronts and the wave energy concentrates itself within the dielectric. A dielectric transmission line employing a metal wave guide as "launcher" is shown in Figure 50. A second metal wave guide at the far end acts as the receiving unit and the microwave energy is carried from there on as if the transmission line had been a metal wave guide over its whole length. Such wave guides, when made of a flexible dielectric such as polyethylene, are very useful for con-

DIELECTRIC GUIDE: LOW WAVE VELOCITY
IN DIELECTRIC TILTS WAVE FRONTS AND
KEEPS ENERGY CONFINED IN ROD

FIG. 49. The confining effect of a dielectric rod results from the lower wave velocity within the rod which tilts the wave fronts inward.

FIG. 50. A length of dielectric wave guide can connect two metallic wave guides.

necting small wave guides together in laboratory experiments.

It is interesting to note that dielectric wave guides have been applied to light waves in the visible region. Here the wavelengths are measured in millionths of an inch; the guide dimensions also must be extremely tiny. A recent development known as fiber optics employs bundles of extremely fine glass fibers. Each fiber transmits nicely the light which falls on one end; hence any image directed against one end of the bundle (the transmitting end) is transmitted faithfully to the receiving end by the entire bundle. The procedure is of interest because the bundle of fibers is flexible and rather unusual things can be done with the technique. That the fiber acts as a true wave guide has been demonstrated through microphotographs of the energy distribution within the fiber. The various electromagnetic mode distributions are clearly visible in the individual fibers.

Acoustic Wave Guides

So far we have considered only wave guides that transport electromagnetic energy. Less useful, but equally possible, are guides transporting sound waves. With them we can show that sound waves exist having properties resembling the polarization properties of electromagnetic waves.

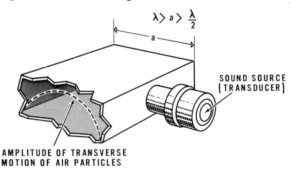

Fig. 51. The first order transverse acoustic mode has a transverse velocity distribution which matches the electric field of a radio wave in a wave guide.

A rectangular guide with a sound source on one side wall is shown in Figure 51. We incorporate the source in the side wall in order to generate a transverse sound wave down the tube. In general, sound waves are longitudinal, causing only back-and-forth motion of the air particles; the vibratory air particle motion is in the direction of travel, not at right angles to it. In the figure we have plotted the magnitude of the side-to-side air particle motion for the transverse wave. Because of the side walls, no transverse motion can occur at those points, and the transverse particle motion is zero. As in the microwave case, if the guide width is less than a wavelength, and more than a half wavelength, only one maximum of side-to-side motion can exist and this occurs at the center of the guide. We observe that this distribution corresponds exactly to the electric-field variation of the dominant electromagnetic mode in a rectangular wave guide. The transverse sound wave also shows the phase and group velocity properties of electromagnetic waves. There remains one difference in the acoustic case: the longitudinal (back-and-forth) mode still can propagate. Special precautions are taken therefore to eliminate this mode when polarization effects are demonstrated with the transverse acoustic mode.

Let us assume then that we have two devices for producing transverse sound waves. Let us use one as a transmitter and one a receiver (Figure 52). When the two units are connected and similarly

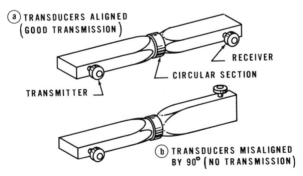

FIG. 52. Transverse sound waves possess polarization characteristics similar to those of electromagnetic waves.

oriented, satisfactory transmission occurs between them. But when one is rotated 90°, the received signal falls to zero. The directions of "polarization" of the two units are at right angles to each other; the transmitter unit cannot induce the proper transverse air particle motion in the receiver unit. Two electromagnetic wave guides would show the same 90° polarization effect.

The procedure we followed with the elliptical tube can be used also with transverse sound waves. The waves, originally produced in a rectangular tube, are conducted first to a round guide and then to a guide having an elliptical cross section, as shown in Figure 53. Employing the same 45° process that was described for microwaves, we can utilize the difference in phase velocities to achieve a 90° rotation of the plane of transverse particle motion. An acoustic half-wave plate is obtained. Again, as in the microwave and optical case, a quarter-wave plate results if the length of the elliptical section is cut in half. "Circularly polarized" sound waves are produced, and the linearly polarized acoustic receiver will receive these waves equally well at any angle.

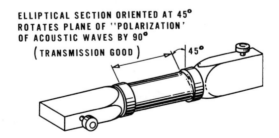

ELLIPTICAL SECTION ORIENTED AT 45°
ROTATES PLANE OF "POLARIZATION'
OF ACOUSTIC WAVES BY 90°
(TRANSMISSION GOOD)   45°

Fig. 53. An elliptical acoustic guide can rotate the plane of vibration of transverse sound waves.

Natural Wave Guides

Counterparts of the dielectric wave guide can be found in nature. We noted that the wave-guide effect exists in the dielectric because the wave velocity is lower within the dielectric than outside it. A structure in which the velocity is low at the axis but increases gradually with the distance out from the axis (instead of abruptly as at the dielectric surface) constitutes a similar guiding means. It continually refocuses back toward the axis energy which may be proceeding away from the axis. This is shown in Figure 54(a); the "tapered" velocity structure behaves like a series of lenses, Figure 54(b).

In the atmosphere above the earth's surface the moisture vapor content often varies with height. This variation causes a pronounced guiding effect

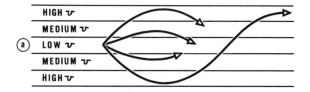

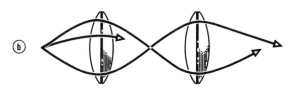

FIG. 54. The proper variation of velocity within a region can create a wave-guiding effect. The region then behaves like a series of lenses.

upon radio waves, particularly those of short wave-length. When this effect is present, unusually long-range transmission occurs. The performance of the radar shown in the upper portion of Figure 55 improves tremendously when a strong meteorological wave-guide "trapping" effect exists; aircraft often can be detected at such distant ranges that they are "over the horizon." Under normal conditions aircraft or other targets beyond the horizon cannot be "seen" because the microwaves used in radar, like light waves, travel in straight lines.

The variations in moisture and air density in our atmosphere also affect the propagation of sound waves. The sound velocity in the atmosphere depends upon the moisture content and density. At a rather high altitude there exists in the earth's atmosphere a relatively permanent "sound channel" where sound is continually refracted back toward the "sound axis," in the way we saw in Figure 54. Exceedingly loud sounds—heavy explosions, for example—can be "heard" at great distances because this acoustic wave guide exists in our atmosphere. Thus large nuclear explosions set off within the atmosphere are detectable thousands of miles away; Figure 56 shows the acoustic record of a megaton nuclear explosion as received 11,500 kilometers away from the blast. The word "heard" is put in quotation marks because the sound waves detected are only the very low frequency sound waves. These cannot be heard by our ears; special detection equipment must be used.

In the very deep portions of the oceans the variation of the water temperature with depth, combined with the effect of gravity, creates a sound "channel" which similarly guides underwater sound signals to very great distances (Figure 56). By virtue of the

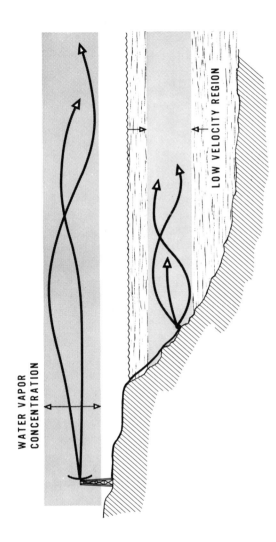

WATER VAPOR
CONCENTRATION

LOW VELOCITY REGION

FIG. 55. The wave-guiding effect of FIG. 54 exists regularly for sound waves in the deep ocean, and occasionally for radio waves in the atmosphere.

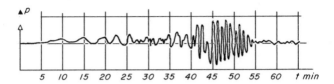

FIG. 56. A nuclear explosion in the atmosphere creates very intense sound waves. These sounds become "trapped" in an atmospheric duct surrounding the earth and can be detected many miles away. This figure is a record of the pressure variation in time excited by a nuclear explosion 11,500 kilometers distant. (After L. Brekhovskikh)

existence of this sound channel in the deep oceans, underwater sound signals have been transmitted and received over paths many hundreds of miles long. When the United States exploded a nuclear bomb in the deep water of the Pacific Ocean (Project Wigwam), echoes of the detonation corresponding to reflections of the sound from the coasts of China and Japan were "heard" off the coast of California. Meteorologists have found this deep sound channel useful. Underwater listening devices can detect the noises made in the central, highly disturbed portion of a typhoon or hurricane hundreds of miles away. The course of the typhoon can be followed by noting the direction or bearing changes of the sound source.

The unusual transmission of radio waves caused by an atmospheric duct is called "anomalous propagation." The deep sound duct in the ocean has been named the "Sofar Channel"; oceanographer Maurice Ewing is credited with its discovery.

Chapter VI

WAVE PATTERNS

In Chapter IV we discussed wave radiation in relation to the radiating devices themselves—horns, lenses, and arrays. Now we shall have a look at the radiation patterns that such wave radiators create in space.

The Optical Slit

First let us consider the case where the energy (and the phase) is uniform over the entire face of the radiator. As shown in Figure 57, such a situation occurs when a distant light source or sound source illuminates a slit in an opaque screen. We want to know what kind of radiation pattern exists in the dark area (the shadow area) behind the screen. The radiation from a horn is shown photographically in Figure 16. Figure 58 shows how radiation emanating from the slit creates an illumination pattern on a second screen. This pattern has a strong central bright area flanked by a series of maxima and minima. It is plotted in Figure 59, and we note the characteristic "side lobes" which we saw prominently in Figure 16 and also in Figure 27. The width of a beam created by waves passing through a slit is inversely proportional to the aperture or slit width a and directly proportional to the wavelength λ. When expressed in degrees, this

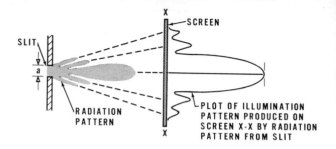

FIG. 57. When a slit in an opaque structure is illuminated by a distant source of light, the energy distribution is uniform over the width of the slit. Also, since the source is quite distant, the circular wave fronts from it can be considered flat (constant-phase) across the slit.

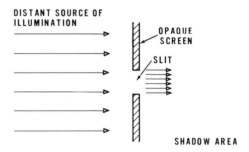

FIG. 58. In the shadow region behind the opaque structure of FIG. 57 light emerges from the slit in a beam-shaped pattern. A screen placed there is illuminated more strongly at the central point than at either side.

beam width is $51\lambda/a$ if a and λ are expressed in the same dimensional units.

Let us see what sort of beam width this figure of $51\lambda/a$ gives in various situations. We shall calculate first the theoretical beam width of the 200-inch optical telescope at Mount Palomar Observatory, in California. In Chapter I we noted that violet light has a wavelength of about 16 millionths of an

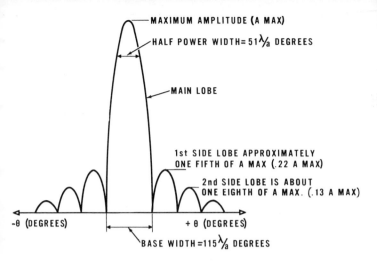

FIG. 59. The pattern of intensity of the illumination falling on the screen of FIG. 58 is here plotted to show more clearly the actual magnitudes of the beam width and minor lobes.

inch. For violet light and the 200-inch mirror, $51\lambda/a$ becomes $51 \times \dfrac{16}{1,000,000} \times \dfrac{1}{200}$ or about 4 millionths of a degree. This calculation says that the 200-inch telescope, if energized uniformly with coherent violet light, would produce a beam which at a point one million miles away would be only 370 feet broad. As a second example, let us calculate the beam width of a radio antenna with an aperture of 20 feet (240 inches) radiating microwaves having a wavelength of ½ inch. Here the expression $51 \times \dfrac{1}{2} \times \dfrac{1}{240}$ corresponds to a beam of about 1/10 of a degree. At a point 57 miles away the microwave beam would be 1/10 of a mile, or 528 feet, wide. For our last example, let us calculate the beam width of a loudspeaker having an aperture of 1 foot and uniformly energized with a tone of 11,000 cycles per second ($\lambda=1/10$ of a foot). The

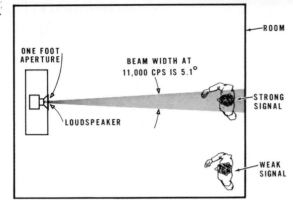

FIG. 60. At high frequencies a loudspeaker having a large radiating dimension provides poor spatial coverage.

expression $51\lambda/a$ shows that the loudspeaker beam would be only 5 degrees wide. The loudspeaker would provide poor room coverage at the high frequencies, since it would direct most of its energy along a rather narrow cone (Figure 60).

The Rectangular Aperture

If we replace the slit in the opaque screen of Figure 58 with a square aperture, we find the beam pattern of Figure 58 then exists in two planes (vertical and horizontal) and a "pencil-shaped" beam results. If we proceed to a rectangular aperture of dimensions a_1 and a_2, we simply insert the correct aperture (a_1 and a_2) in the expression $51\lambda/a$ to obtain the beam width in each plane. In this case the beam has an oval cross section (often called a "fan" beam).

The foregoing analysis brings out a rather interesting fact that often causes confusion. *The oval beam of a rectangular aperture is not oriented the*

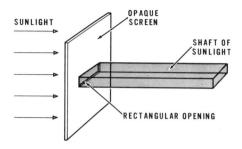

FIG. 61. Sunlight passing through a rectangular aperture creates a rectangular shaft of light whose orientation matches that of the aperture.

way we would expect it to be. In Figure 61 is shown a shaft of sunlight produced by a rectangular opening in an opaque screen. We see that the shaft dimensions and orientation match the dimensions of the opening. Figure 62 portrays a horn with a rectangular mouth of dimensions a_1 (small) and a_2 (large). The beam width, given by $51\lambda/a$, is large for the smaller dimension a_1 and small (narrower) for the larger aperture dimension a_2. Here, then, the beam shape is rotated just 90° from the orientation of the shaft of sunlight. We shall see that the shaft of sunlight retains its pattern orientation because both aperture dimensions are tremendously large in terms of wavelength and the pattern we observe is in the *near field*. We are so close to the aperture through which the shaft of sunlight is passing that the pattern which would be observed at a distant point has not had opportunity to establish itself. We shall discuss this effect in more detail later in the chapter. The *far field* for the sunlight example exists only at tremendous distances from the rectangular opening. There, of course, the beam would exhibit the character shown in Figure 62, the sharper beam corresponding to the broader aperture dimension.

Gain

It is useful to be able to designate how effectively radiators concentrate their energy in a beam pattern. The term *gain* is used to indicate the improvement over a radiator that has no beam effect. The latter radiator, which radiates equally in all directions, is called an *isotropic* radiator. The gain of a broadside radiator is proportional to its area and inversely proportional to the square of the wave-

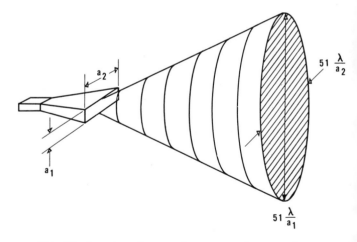

FIG. 62. A rectangular sound wave or microwave horn produces a beam of oval cross section whose orientation does *not* match the orientation of the aperture.

length. A square radiator 100 wavelengths on a side can beam energy to a distant point about 120,000 times more effectively than an isotropic radiator. This is the same as saying that if the power in the square radiator were to be reduced by a factor of 120,000, the radiated signal still would be received as well as from an isotropic radiator transmitting the original high power.

Since "gain" is just as effective in receiving as in radiating or transmitting, a transmission link benefits from the *product* of the gains of the radiating antenna and the receiving antenna. At radio broadcasting frequencies the wavelengths are so long that high gain radiating structures are not feasible. The amount of electrical power transmitted from radio broadcasting stations accordingly runs up into the hundreds of thousands of watts. In contrast, microwave links need power of only a few watts. They employ wavelengths a few inches long and transmitting and receiving antennas having 10-foot apertures. The radiators achieve individual gains of ten thousand or so and exhibit gain *products* exceeding 100 million (Figure 63).

With the recent advent of the *laser,* or optical maser, it has become possible to generate light waves possessing a high degree of coherency. The various considerations for gain and beam width we have discussed apply equally well to any coherent radiation. Accordingly, the extremely short wavelengths of the light waves employed in a laser achieve fantastically high gain values because, as we saw, gain is inversely proportional to the wavelength squared.

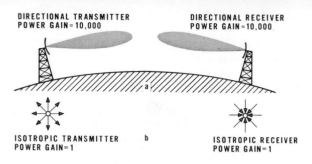

DIRECTIONAL TRANSMITTER
POWER GAIN = 10,000

DIRECTIONAL RECEIVER
POWER GAIN = 10,000

a

ISOTROPIC TRANSMITTER
POWER GAIN = 1

b

ISOTROPIC RECEIVER
POWER GAIN = 1

TO HAVE SAME POWER RECEIVED IN
(b) AS IN (a) TRANSMITTED POWER IN
(b) MUST BE INCREASED
10,000 X 10,000 OR 100 MILLION TIMES

Fig. 63. Microwave relay transmission links 25 to 30 miles in length are widely used for network television and telephone communication purposes. High-gain radiating and receiving horn-lens antennas permit use of very low-power transmitters.

Tapered Illumination

In Figure 59 we observed strong sides lobes in the pattern of a uniformly energized or illuminated slit. In some applications a high side lobe level is objectionable, and a process known as illumination tapering is employed to suppress the side lobes. For example, in radar applications when a parabolic *dish* is used as a radar antenna, the wave guide at its focal point is often equipped with a horn whose directivity leads to a tapered illumination. The horn causes the radiated energy to concentrate more at the center of the dish than at the edges (Figure 64), and the side lobe level is thereby reduced.

Tapers have one disadvantage; they lower the gain of the aperture. Maximum gain requires uniform illumination. However, because side lobe level is a rather important consideration, gains of about

a half of this maximum value are usually accepta-
ble in microwave applications.

Near Field Patterns

We mentioned that the pattern of Figure 59 was
the pattern observed at a distant point. The region
far from the radiator is named the *Fraunhofer* region for the early nineteenth-century Bavarian scientist Joseph Fraunhofer. Near the radiator the pattern exhibits marked changes in its character, and
the far field or Fraunhofer pattern is generally considered to be established adequately only at distances exceeding $2a^2/\lambda$. For a 100-wavelength aperture the Fraunhofer region thus begins at a point
20,000 wavelengths from the radiator. For a 5-
wavelength aperture, it begins at a point 50 wavelengths away.

The field near the radiator is named for the

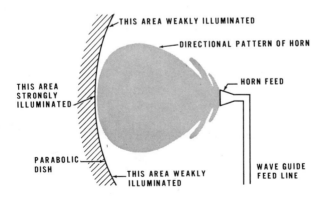

FIG. 64. A small horn placed at the focus of a parabolic
reflector produces a tapered illumination because of the
directive effect present even in the small horn.

French engineer and scientist Augustin Jean Fresnel, a contemporary of Fraunhofer. It extends from the aperture to a distance equal to $a^2/2\lambda$—i.e., to a point one-fourth of the distance to where the Fraunhofer pattern starts. The region from $a^2/2\lambda$ to $2a^2/\lambda$ is called the *transition region*. In the immediate vicinity of the aperture of the radiator the radiation intensity matches the intensity across the aperture itself. Thus, just as the shaft of sunlight of Figure 61 matches the rectangular aperture producing it, so the radiation immediately behind the slit of Figure 58 exhibits an intensity distribution almost as uniform as at the slit itself. Just as the water stream issuing at high pressure from the mouth of a fire hose remains cylindrical and equal in cross section to the cross section of the hose and its nozzle, so the issuing light beam maintains *its* cross-sectional area for some distance upon emerging from an aperture. And, just as the water stream eventually sprays out into a broader pattern, so, at some distance from the aperture, the light beam begins to spread out, thereby generating the pattern observed at a great distance away. This maintenance of cross-sectional area (of the water stream or the light beam) is called "collimation." When the waves pass through the slit they remain "collimated" for a while, and within the Fresnel region very little energy "spreading" takes place. The amplitude distribution shifts gradually from its uniform value immediately in the vicinity of the radiator toward its final illumination observed in the distant Fraunhofer region.

We see now why the shaft of sunlight of Figure 61 retains the shape of the rectangular slit which creates it. Since light wavelengths are measured in millionths of inches, the Fresnel region for apertures that are inches in size extends millions of inches or many miles from the aperture. The shaft which we observe is the *very* close-in region where an insignificant amount of beam spreading has occurred.

Diverging Wave Patterns

Up to now, we have considered radiators designed to produce flat wave fronts so that maximum energy could be radiated to large distances in a given direction. This situation is the opposite of what is desired in a loudspeaker. A loudspeaker should spread the sound uniformly throughout the room, rather than aim it in a given direction. But to be effective at the lower frequencies, loudspeakers generally must have rather large apertures, and this configuration makes them quite directional for the higher frequency sounds of short wavelength. We can see in Figure 16 how directional a six-inch aperture horn is at 9000 cycles per second.

One way to improve the situation is to use more than one loudspeaker to cover the large frequency band of audible sound. The units used for the high frequencies can then be smaller and therefore less directional. High frequency speakers also can be made with rectangular apertures. Then, as we saw in Figure 62, the narrow dimension (and broad beam) can be oriented horizontally so as to cover 90° to 180° of the horizontal dimension of the room. The more directional large aperture then will be oriented vertically, but this is not too serious since coverage in the vertical plane is less demanding. It is interesting to note that until recently, and because of the confusion we discussed earlier, rectangular high frequency loudspeakers were always oriented as shown in Figure 62. Everyone assumed that the wide dimension gave the wider beam. Nowadays this practice has been almost universally corrected, albeit grudgingly (and sheepishly!), and in the better high-fidelity sets high frequency rectangular aperture loudspeakers are always placed with the long dimension vertical.

A second way to avoid directivity is to generate curved wave fronts across the loudspeaker aperture by means of a diverging lens. Just as the diverging glass lens of optics causes a diverging of the light rays (in contrast to the convergence or concentration of rays caused by the usual focusing lens), so a diverging acoustic lens spreads the acoustic energy from a loudspeaker to provide superior spatial coverage. This is illustrated in Figure 65. Here it is shown that a horn radiator produces a directing or concentration of energy in the direction in which it is pointed because it generates emerging wave fronts that are relatively flat. When, however, a divergent lens is placed before the horn, a strong wave-front curvature is produced at the aperture, and this curvature results in a definite improvement in the angular sound coverage of the loudspeaker (or, in this case, horn). The same lens can correct the beaming effect of other types of loudspeakers. Figure 66 shows the lens placed before a cone-type loudspeaker mounted in its cabinet.

Wave Patterns of Incoherent and Coherent Light Sources

One difference that has existed, at least until quite recently, between light on the one hand and sound and microwaves on the other involves the coherence of the sources of these three classes of radiation. Coherence itself has several meanings, so to under-

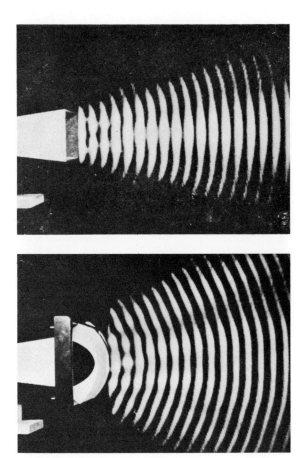

FIG. 65. The flat wave fronts present in the beam of FIG. 16 are responsible for the directional effect (above). A diverging acoustic lens generates curved wave fronts and improves the angular coverage of the radiated sound (below).

FIG. 66. A diverging acoustic lens placed before a loud-speaker prevents the "beaming" effect normally present for high frequency sounds.

stand the situation we shall discuss this feature of coherence through the use of examples.

In sound or microwaves, we can build sources of the order of one wavelength or less in size. Thus the wave guides for radio waves we discussed earlier had cross-sectional dimensions comparable to a wavelength, and in acoustics, too, we can devise sound generators of almost any size. Light wavelengths, however, are extremely minute, and even to consider constructing a "light generator" the size of one light wavelength would be preposterous. Yet for microwaves it was just this very ability to start with a small wave generator that enabled designers to achieve the high values of gain and narrow beam widths predicted by theory. By starting with a "one-wavelength" generator and using horns in combination with lenses or parabolic reflectors, it is possible to create a completely uniform-phase wave front the size of the radiator. The beam width is then determined only by the size of the final radiating device, at the wavelength.

Because the usual light sources, such as arc lights or incandescent lamps, have a luminous area that is extremely large compared to a wavelength, a parabolic reflector, even if optically perfect in shape, cannot produce a "perfect" beam. The extended area of the light source automatically results in the production of broad beams, and the amount of the broadening can be ascertained directly from the geometrical relationship existing between the source size, the reflector size, and the focal length of the reflector.

Now suppose that two choices exist for a light source. One is an arc light with a luminous area a half inch across and the other is a luminous rod made of special glass or of ruby also a half inch across.

Suppose further that a distinct difference exists in the way the light is produced across the two half-inch areas. In the arc, light is generated randomly at millions of tiny points on the crater of the arc. Each of these tiny sources of light is independent of the others, in phase characteristics, in amplitude characteristics, and in time. Suppose, on the other hand, that all the light from the end face of the luminous rod is the result of plane light waves, and that this light as it emerges from the rod is in the form of waves similar to the plane sound waves shown emerging from the right side of the lens of Figure 33.

The waves from the arc light are called incoherent, because each tiny independent source interferes in a highly random way with all its neighbors. The waves we described for the ruby rod, however, are coherent: each element of the wave has a definite and uniform phase relation to its neighbors.

Just a few years back our hypothetical coherent light source was still only hypothetical. Today the ruby-rod or glass-rod laser can be found in laboratories all over the world. With the rod-type laser extremely high degrees of coherency can be obtained. An even greater coherency is possible with another type, the gas laser.

The possibilities of the coherent light waves generated in the ruby rod are evident when we consider that even the half-inch dimension of the rod yields, according to the formula $51\lambda/a$, a beam width of one two-thousandths of a degree. Furthermore, the plane light waves emitted from a laser can be focused to a point just as waves were focused in Figure 34. Focal areas a few light wavelengths

FIG. 67. A steel razor blade disintegrates when the coherent light waves from a ruby laser are focused sharply on it.

across can be achieved, and the enormous energy concentration in such small areas can cause very unusual things to happen. The photo in Figure 67 shows what a focused beam of light from a laser can do to a steel razor blade. The concentration of energy is so great at that spot that the metal disintegrates.

The tiny focal area created by focusing a laser beam to a point can be thought of now as a new light source of extremely small dimensions. We have overcome the limitations that existed in the past on light sources. The light beams we can now create by placing one of these wavelength-size light sources at the focal point of a parabolic mirror or lens afford the perfection we have had for microwave and sound-wave beams. The phenomena of light, sound, and radio are intermingled even more than they have been in the past, and the wave techniques developed by microwave and acoustic scientists have become of significant importance to physicists working in the field of light waves.

Chapter VII

WAVE REFRACTORS

With the insight gained from Chapter III's discussion of the refraction of waves by prisms and lenses, we can proceed now to examine some of the materials and structures used in optics to focus light waves, in radio for microwaves, and in acoustics for high frequency sound waves. The discussion of certain of the refracting materials will emphasize again the strong analogy between the behavior of light waves and the behavior of sound waves.

Acquaintance with the focusing properties of transparent materials like glass when ground into certain geometrical shapes goes back to very ancient times. The great Archimedes (*c.* 287–212 B.C.) proposed to destroy enemy warships with a "burning glass" that would concentrate the sun's rays, and hence its energy, sharply enough to set fire to wood some distance away. Nowadays glass is almost universally used for lenses designed to focus light waves in the visible range. A few inexpensive magnifying glasses are made of clear plastic, but they are the exception. Cameras, binoculars, eyeglasses, and most optical telescopes all have lenses of high quality glass to achieve the desired focusing effect.

When it became possible to generate radio wavelengths short enough for effective focusing by parabolic reflectors, it was a natural next step to think about lenses. Glass, it turned out, was not as desirable at microwaves as some plastic materials which exhibited lower loss. Polystyrene and polyethylene, both extremely loss-free in electrical circuits, became the popular dielectrics for microwave lenses and for radar-antenna covers. These covers were called radomes (radar domes); their purpose was to protect the radar antennas from weather and wind effects without interfering with the passage of the radio waves.

Scientists demonstrated quite early that sound waves too respond to the focusing action of lenses. Rubber balloons filled with gas focus sound waves just as a glass lens focuses light waves if the velocity of sound in the gas is lower than it is in air. Most current designs of acoustic lenses, however, rely on special rigid structures to achieve the focusing effect. Inasmuch as these rigid acoustic lenses are largely outgrowths of earlier microwave lens developments, it will be appropriate to discuss various microwave lenses first.

Wave-guide Lenses

As microwave antennas grew in size, the weight of natural dielectrics such as glass or polystyrene began to place dielectric lenses at a disadvantage relative to the lighter weight parabolic dish structures. A ten-foot-diameter lens made of polystyrene would weigh several tons, far more than the equivalent aluminum reflector. Accordingly, several lightweight refracting structures were developed for use with microwaves; microwave designers then could take advantage of certain properties of lenses.

The first such lens "material" utilized the higher phase velocity property of wave guides. As we noted earlier, the velocity of microwaves confined in tubes

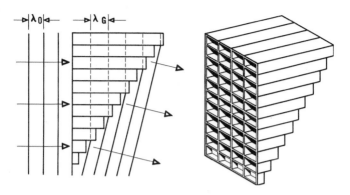

FIG. 68. A wedge-shaped stack of wave guides acts as a prism because of the higher wave velocity within the wave guides.

gets a little mixed up; within the guide the energy travels more slowly than in free space but the wave crests themselves travel faster. Since the process of focusing modifies the wave fronts, it is this second velocity that we deal with when we use wave-guide effects for lenses.

To see how wave guides can be used to refract microwaves, let us imagine a stack of rectangular wave guides cut to proper length and placed side by side, as shown in Figure 68. Let us assume that waves with flat wave fronts arrive from the left and emerge at the right. We see in the figure that the higher wave velocity within the guide (indicated in the figure by the longer guide wavelength λ_g) will impart a tilt to the wave front as the waves leave the assemblage. The structure thus behaves, for microwaves, like a prism, and this "refracting"

102

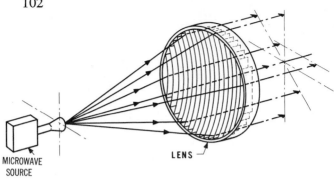

MICROWAVE
SOURCE

LENS

FIG. 69. Removal of the top and bottom wall of the wave guides of FIG. 68 results in a simple metal plate structure. When such structures are shaped to a proper profile they constitute a microwave lens.

property of wave guides can be, and has been, used widely in the construction of lenses of various types and sizes.

In a rectangular wave guide the existence of the higher phase velocity is not dependent upon the presence of the top and bottom walls of the guide. Wave-guide lenses therefore are made usually of sheets of metal, as shown in Figure 69. An actual lens of this type is shown in Figure 70. Eighteen inches in diameter, it was constructed at the time of World War II and was, to the author's best knowledge, the first two-dimensional wave-guide lens. Successful tests of this structure encouraged further exploration of numerous variations. In Figure 23 the microwaves shown are being focused by a similar metal-plate (wave-guide) lens. Both illustrations bring out the fact that lenses making use of the increased wave-velocity property of wave guides must

FIG. 70. The first two-dimensional metal plate microwave lens, shown here, was built during World War II.

be thick at the edge and thin at the center, the exact converse of a glass lens.

To reduce further the weight of wave-guide metal-plate lenses, the process called "stepping" was developed. In an unstepped circular lens, starting at the center of the lens and moving outward toward the rim, one finds that the thickness increases continuously. In a stepped lens, "setbacks," where the lens thickness is reduced abruptly, are incorporated. Such steps are feasible in microwave lenses because most microwave systems center on a given radio frequency or wavelength. The step design is based on one given wavelength; it works well for that wavelength but not for quite different wavelengths. The pattern for the step design is as follows: starting from the center of the circular lens, the thickness increases according to certain equations until the thickness increase equals one design wavelength as measured within the lens—that is, one guide wavelength. At this point the lens thickness can be reduced by a step to its original center thickness. At succeeding points, wherever the thickness increase again equals a guide wavelength, succeeding steps are introduced. Figure 71 shows a circular stepped lens used in ship-borne radar, its thickness held down through the stepping procedure. A square stepped lens is shown in Figure 72. It is a prototype of the lens employed in the first microwave radio-relay circuit operated by the Bell System between New York and Boston. This circuit included seven relay stations, each having four ten-foot-square lenses of this type. The microwave frequencies used were centered at 4000 million cycles per second; since one telephone voice channel re-

Fig. 71. The "stepping" configuration to reduce the thickness of large-aperture wave-guide lenses can be seen in this illustration. This lens was used in a radar employing microwaves having a wavelength of one-half inch.

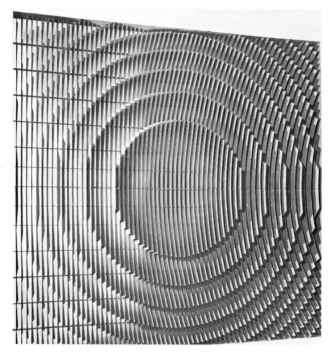

Fig. 72. Square-aperture lenses are used in horn-lens antennas in which the advantageous shielding effect of the horn is exploited.

quires a bandwidth* of only 4000 cycles, this circuit with its extremely high center frequency could accommodate simultaneously hundreds of separate telephone conversations. One of the stainless-steel horns employed in this New York to Boston relay circuit is shown in Figure 73; the ten-foot-by-ten-foot lens is placed in the mouth of the horn. Figure 74 is a photograph taken by placing a camera in the throat of the horn. Several of the steps of the wave-guide lens can be seen. The horizontal black strips are supports to maintain accurate spacing of the vertical wave-guide plates. This horn-lens antenna was developed at the Holmdel, New Jersey, Bell Laboratories (the background in the photo is the New Jersey countryside). Figure 75 is a photo of a stepped lens whose long dimension, 20 feet, corresponds to an aperture of 480 wavelengths at the design frequency. Constructed at about the end of World War II, it produced a beam width of 1/10 of a degree, at that time the sharpest of any microwave antenna in existence.

The higher-velocity property of wave guides also permits the design of lenses of constant thickness. The index of refraction of natural materials such as

---

* Bandwidth is an expression denoting the width of the frequency band required to transmit a given type of signal. Thus the bandwidth for a telegraph signal (where only dots and dashes are transmitted) is rather small, only a few hundred cycles per second or less. A bandwidth of 4000 cycles per second has proved satisfactory for telephone speech. Hi-fi enthusiasts insist on an "audio" bandwidth equaling our full hearing range, and this extends from perhaps 30 cycles per second to 15 or 20 thousand cycles per second. Television signals are much more complicated; they demand a bandwidth of almost 5 *million* cycles per second.

FIG. 73. The author is seen here beside the pyramidal horn and wave-guide lens developed for the first New York-Boston microwave radio relay link. The metal lens is ten feet square.

Fig. 74. A view from the horn throat of the antenna of Fig. 73 shows the stepped structure of the lens.

FIG. 75. This cylindrical lens, twenty feet long, produced the sharpest microwave beam of its day. The man is the designer of the lens, W. M. Sharpless, of Bell Telephone Laboratories.

Fig. 76. A focusing lens having uniform thickness utilizes the variation in wave-guide width to provide the required refractive effect.

glass is fixed, and the lens designer is limited to variations in the thickness of a glass lens to achieve the desired focusing effect. Within a wave guide, however, the wave velocity changes as the wave-guide width changes; a narrow guide has a stronger refractive effect than a wide guide. The lens of Figure 76 makes use of this property of wave guides. At the center of the lens the wave guides have their maximum width; at the edges they are narrow. The greater refractive effect obtained at the edge of the lens of Figure 70 by increased thickness is here duplicated by the use of narrower wave-guide widths.

Artificial Dielectrics

One limitation of "wave-guide dielectrics" stems from the fact that the wave velocity within a wave guide is dependent upon frequency. We noted, for example, that as the guide width approaches a half wavelength, the wave velocity becomes quite high. This property of variation of wave velocity (refractive index) with frequency is called dispersion. In optical lenses dispersion is annoying, because it causes rays of different colors to focus at different focal points. It is called chromatic aberration; if severe, it can, in a camera for example, cause a blurred picture. Dispersion is annoying also in microwave lenses because it limits the frequency spread of the signal for which the microwave system is designed. Waves whose frequencies are too different from the design frequency are not focused at the design focal point; they therefore are not radiated or received efficiently by the lens. Microwave relay systems employing lenses which exhibit severe dispersion can handle only a limited frequency band.

Accordingly, a definite need existed for a light-weight lens material that would be free of the objectionable dispersion of wave-guide lenses. Since necessity is the mother of invention, structures called "artificial" dielectrics, or metallic "delay" materials were developed. They behave like a true dielectric in that the waves are delayed; the wave velocity is less than the free-space velocity. Like polystyrene or polyethylene, these materials also possess low loss factors. A discussion of the physical principles underlying these artificial materials will help us to understand why ordinary materials (such as glass) delay and hence refract light waves.

How do true dielectrics affect waves? It was an inquiry into this process that brought about the development of artificial dielectrics. The results of the inquiry suggested an effort to scale up minute structures known to exist in crystalline materials, and an entire family of artificial dielectrics resulted. We shall follow this original inquiry and analysis in our discussion.

All substances are composed of assemblages of very tiny particles (atoms and molecules). These particles or groups of particles have electric charges; they are affected therefore by the presence of an electric field. If, as in Figure 77, we place a tiny particle of material between the plates of a charged electrical condenser, we find that the particle becomes strained or distorted. The negatively charged units in the particle are attracted by the positive plate of the condenser and vice versa. If we reverse the polarity of voltage applied to the condenser plates, the particle is strained in the reverse direction.

Now electromagnetic waves (light waves or microwaves) establish electric fields similar to the

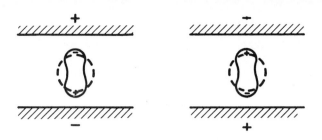

FIG. 77. The charged particles of a molecule of glass or dielectric are attracted to the oppositely charged plates of a condenser. Reversal of the electric field (at the right) reverses the direction of stress on the molecules.

electric field existing between the plates of a charged condenser. In the wave case, however, the polarity of the electric field reverses at a rate that depends upon the frequency of the electromagnetic wave. Thus for our 60-cycle house current the electric current is alternating at a rate of 60 alternations per second—that is, the electric field *it* would create across the plates of a condenser would change direction 60 times a second. For microwaves propagating within a wave guide, the top and bottom walls of the guide act like the parallel plates of a condenser. In this case the electric field between the "plates" is alternating or reversing itself at the rate of several thousand million times a second. This field reversal continues to exist even after the waves emerge from the wave guide and are propagating in free space. A similar but even faster field reversal is created in space by light waves. Since violet light has a frequency of 7.37×10^{14} cycles per second, one of our tiny particles placed in the path of waves of violet light would experience an electric field reversal 7×10^{14} times a second. Because every action has an equal and opposite reaction, the rapid reversals of strain on the particle react on the light wave and reduce its

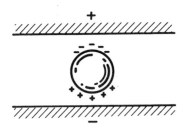

Fig. 78. When a conducting sphere is in an electric field the free electric charges on the surface of the sphere cause it to behave like the molecule of dielectric of Fig. 77.

velocity of propagation. Thus light moves through glass at about two thirds of its velocity in air or vacuum. Lower-frequency electromagnetic waves experience this same effect, and glass accordingly exhibits the same refractive index (or wave velocity reduction) for microwaves as it does for light waves.

Since the wavelengths of microwaves are in inches compared to millionths of an inch for visible light, an obvious question follows. Cannot the particles involved in the refractive process be made much larger if we are dealing with microwaves rather than light waves? An affirmative answer appeared likely, and the first artificial dielectrics were put together accordingly. It was decided that the first particles to be tried would be conducting *spheres,* since it seemed that between the plates of a condenser (Figure 78) such spheres would act very much like the molecules of a true dielectric. For the assembly of conducting spheres to simulate the molecular crystal lattice properly they were spaced apart and insulated from one another. Individual beads from strands of inexpensive artificial pearls were used for one quite successful lens; the beads were coated with a silver conducting paint, and then mounted on thin wooden sticks to form the lattice. This lens is shown in Figure 79. Because the number of spheres in this lens was small, the ideal lenticular shape of the assemblage could only be approximated. However, the focusing action was quite pronounced. This success led to a second type of "spherical molecule" lens. In this lens, steel ball bearings constituted the elements, and polystyrene foam supported the spheres in their three-dimensional lattice. This lens is shown in Figure 80. The sphere having symmetry in three dimensions, these first dielectrics were homogeneous or isotropic; they exhibited the same properties for all waves, regardless of direction or polarization. Because designers of a microwave system have control both over the direction of a propagation and the polarization of the microwaves used in the system, this isotropy feature is in many cases not required. If the lens can be designed more simply and more inexpensively for a particular need, so much the better. Thus, if disks are substituted for the spheres, a weight advantage results; when they are mounted to present their maximum area to the incoming wave, an effect quite similar to that of spheres is obtained. An open-structure disk lens is shown in Figure 81. A further reduction in weight was achieved by making the lens disks of thin, lightweight metal foil. Figure 82 shows such a lens with copper foil disks supported on circular polystyrene foam slabs. It is the lens employed in Figure 83.

Both spheres and properly oriented disks create the desired delay effect for waves of all polarizations. However, a lens that can focus only vertically polarized waves may have important uses. The strip lens is such a lens. If we imagine the disks

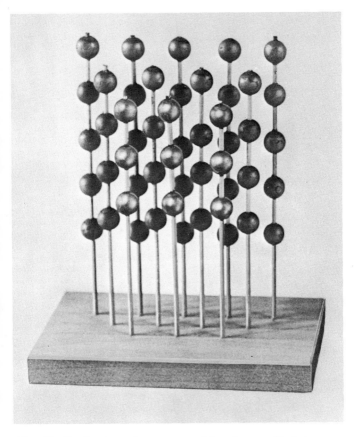

Fig. 79. Conducting spheres arranged in a lens profile bring microwaves to a focus.

FIG. 80. A lightweight foamed dielectric can support the conducting spheres that constitute the active focusing portion of a microwave lens.

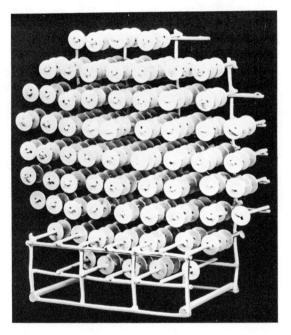

Fɪɢ. 81. Conducting disks, when oriented as shown and arranged in a lens profile, focus microwaves.

FIG. 82. Copper foil disks affixed to circular foam slabs compose a very lightweight microwave lens.

of the lens of Figure 82 joined together along horizontal lines, we arrive at the strip lens of Figure 83.

Very large strip lenses, using foam to support the thin metal strips, are employed on the Bell Telephone System's extension of the New York-Boston microwave relay links to transcontinental use. One of the cross-continental relay system's towers is shown in Figure 84; three of the four horn-lens antennas of the kind used in each two-way relay station are visible. Because of the lack of dispersion in the artificial dielectric lenses, these later extensions of the Bell System's relay network can handle a broader frequency band (more telephone conversations) than could be handled by the original New York to Boston portion.

The strip technique can be used to obtain artificial dielectrics which exhibit a very high refractive index. Most natural materials such as glass or plastics possess indices of refraction of about one and a half or so; a natural material of high index is rather unusual. In the construction of the lens of Figure 85 the metal strips were placed very close together, affixed to thin transparent plastic sheets, and then the plastic sheets were placed in juxtaposition. The metal strips were made to overlap also, and the plastic sheets furnished the insulation needed to prevent them from touching and "short-circuiting" the electric field of the microwaves. In this lens a refractive index ten times that of glass was realized.

Path-length Lenses

Another lightweight microwave lens merits discussion because it is particularly adaptable to acous-

FIG. 83. When the disks of FIG. 81 are made horizontally continuous, the conducting strip microwave lens results.

FIG. 84. The microwave relay towers which transmit telephone and network television signals from coast to coast
have horn antennas with lenses in their apertures. The lens
material is an artificial dielectric consisting of metal foil
strips supported in plastic foam.

124

FIG. 85. Conducting strips placed very close together and overlapping form a highly refractive medium. This microwave lens, using thin celluloid sheets as spacers between the strips, has an effective dielectric constant of 225.

tic waves. It is called the *path-length lens* because its operation is based on control of travel times to make the path lengths of the focused waves equal. The design profile shown in Figure 39 was obtained by calculation of the times taken by all rays in their travel from the focus to a plane. The lens of that figure was an ordinary glass lens, and the lower velocity of the waves as they passed through the glass accounted for the extra time needed by the center rays. The wave travel time can be controlled also by forcing them to travel longer paths at their normal free-space velocity. Figure 86 shows a structure that accomplishes this. Flat plates, a large number of them, are set at an angle and their contour shaped so as to produce a lenticular outline (thick at the center, thin at the edge). A cross section of this lens through its center portion is shown in Figure 87. Since no dielectric is employed, the waves always travel at their normal free space velocity. However, they are constrained to travel the longer, diagonal path within the lens structure. When they emerge at the right, the resulting wave front is practically identical to that formed by a dielectric lens in which the waves travel unconstrained and at lower velocity. As in the glass lens of Figure 39, the profile is again a hyperbola.

The constraining members constituting this particular lens are thin conducting sheets, and the microwaves being focused pass between them quite easily if their electric-field vector lies in a plane perpendicular to the plates, as indicated in Figure 87. The equivalent index of refraction of this type of structure is determined by the angle the plates make with the horizontal. It is this angle that specifies how much longer the actual wave path is in relation

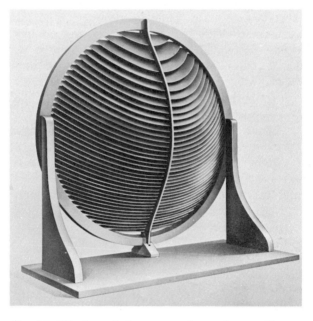

FIG. 86. Tilted metal plates cut to form a lens profile create a longer path for microwaves and cause focusing.

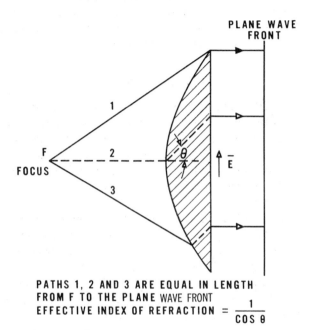

PATHS 1, 2 AND 3 ARE EQUAL IN LENGTH
FROM F TO THE PLANE WAVE FRONT
EFFECTIVE INDEX OF REFRACTION $= \dfrac{1}{\cos\theta}$

FIG. 87. A cross-sectional view of the lens of FIG. 86 reveals how all rays have the same path length from focus to plane wave front. Dotted lines show paths of 2 and 3 through lens.

to the direct unconstrained path that the waves would have taken if the lens were absent. Because of its relative simplicity, this lens has been employed also in microwave relay applications. Figure 88 shows a close-up of such a lens designed in Japan for relay use, and a relay installation of four such horn-lens antennas, also Japanese.

Acoustic Refractors

All the three forms of microwave refractors just discussed can also focus sound waves. We shall not dwell at length on the use of the wave-guide type of lens in acoustics. Because they involve transverse acoustic modes, they possess bandwidth limitations and are accordingly not too useful in practical applications.

The various artificial dielectrics offer broad-band acoustic refracting structures and are quite effective in focusing sound waves encompassing broad-frequency bands. We have seen the strip form of refractor of Figure 83 focus sound waves in Figure 34. Also, Figure 31 shows sound waves being refracted by a strip prism. For sound waves no foam supporting structure can be used, as was done in constructing the microwave lens shown in Figure 82. Rather, the lens must be of an open configuration so that only the elements of the delay structure act upon the sound waves. Both disk and strip structures are quite satisfactory.

Figure 89 shows sound waves being formed into a beam by an open-structure strip lens. In this figure the side lobes of the beam can be seen, but only faintly. These side lobes are much more strongly emphasized in Figure 90; it is a photograph in which the phase technique was employed. To in-

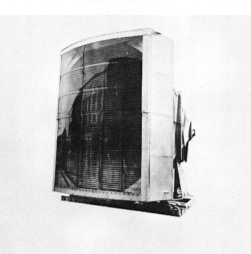

FIG. 88. In Japan path-length lenses have been put to use in microwave radio relay applications. The top photograph shows the slant plate construction similar to that in FIG. 86. (*Courtesy of Mitsubishi Electric Manufacturing Co. and Nippon Telephone and Telegraph Public Corporation.*)

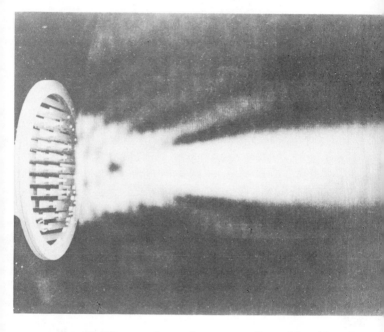

FIG. 89. When weak sound waves are focused by this strip lens, the amplitude pattern shows only small vestiges of the actual side lobes.

FIG. 90. Intense sound waves create this pattern, with the large number of side lobes now quite evident. In this photo, the phase of the wave fronts is portrayed. It indicates that phase reversals occur between the main lobe and successive side lobes.

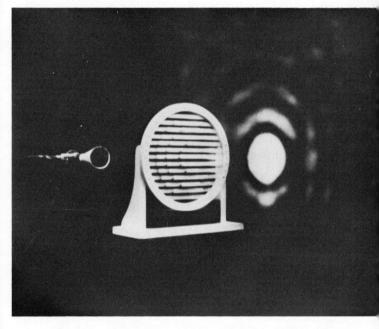

Fig. 91. By sampling the sound field in a plane perpendicular to the direction of the waves, we portray a cross section of the main lobe and side lobes. The side lobes are seen to be annular cones of sound surrounding the solid sound cone of the main lobe.

dicate that the beam formed by this lens is sharp
in both the vertical and horizontal planes, the record of Figure 91 was made. In this photo the probe
microphone scanned in a plane parallel to the plane
of the lens, rather than in the perpendicular plane
of previous photographs. The circular cross section
of the beam is evident and the side "lobes" are seen
to be cones with annular cross sections.

The strip technique can be used to focus sound
waves in a way not feasible for microwaves. If the
strips are made to run in both the vertical and
horizontal directions, the equivalent of metal sheets
having square holes results. Such a lens is shown in
Figure 92. These sheets are perfectly transparent for
sound waves and provide the same delaying action
that was achieved with strips running in only one
direction. The lens thus focuses sound waves quite
nicely. The lens is *not* effective for microwaves,
however, because of the polarized nature of electromagnetic waves. As we have seen, microwaves
generate an electric field as they propagate, and this
electric field would be "short-circuited" by a conductor parallel to this varying field. Just as a wire
connecting the two plates of a condenser would
short-circuit the condenser (as it would short-circuit the two wires of our 60-cycle house current),
so a conducting rod running between the centers of
the top and bottom walls of a wave guide would
short-circuit the microwave energy. Longer vertical
conductors in free space would similarly short-circuit vertically polarized microwaves.

Whereas the "molecules" of an artificial dielectric
must be conducting for microwaves, for sound
waves they must be *immovable* or *rigid*. Sound
waves, like water waves, are mechanical in nature;
they are reflected by a hard, rigid wall. On the other

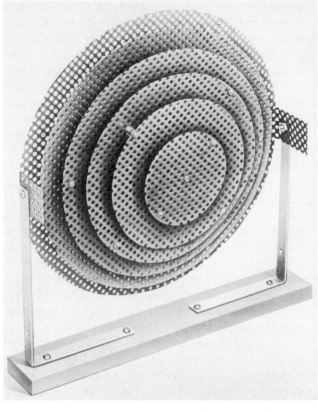

FIG. 92. This lens can focus sound waves, but not electro-magnetic waves. It can be thought of as a strip lens in which the strips run both vertically and horizontally.

hand, the light particles in a smoke-filled room present no obstacle to the progress of a propagating sound wave. Thus in general, sound waves are influenced only by something that is rigid or immovable. Electromagnetic waves can be influenced strongly only by electrical conductors, such as a copper wire or polished metal surfaces. When we insert the two ends of a heavy copper wire into our 60-cycle outlet, we blow a fuse; similarly, a polished metal surface stops (reflects) light waves and microwaves. We find, experimentally, that a nonconducting wall (such as the wall of a house) has little effect upon radio waves; they pass right through and reach portable radio receivers. Similarly, we know that thin fiberboard walls in a hotel room do not block out the noise of the adjoining rooms. To influence sound waves the object must be heavy or immovable, and to influence electrical waves the object must be a good electrical conductor. For the strip structures exactly the same design equations hold for microwaves as for sound waves. In the equations it is the wavelength and not the frequency that is related. It is interesting to note that this equivalence of light and sound was set forth many years ago by Lord Rayleigh. In analyzing certain problems of diffraction and refraction, he often worked with both types of waves at the same time. He referred to sound waves as "aerial waves of condensation and rarefaction," and to light waves as "electrical waves propagated in the dielectric." It was Rayleigh who first stated that in the passage of waves through a slit the same results are obtained for aerial waves or electrical waves if the screen is rigid or perfectly conducting, respectively.

The microwave structure that has found the

greatest use in acoustic lens applications is the slant plate or path-length lens. It is easy to see from our analysis of Figure 87 that such structures should function in exactly the same way for sound waves and microwaves, since both waves are forced to travel the longer paths. Besides, since normal sound waves have no polarization properties, polarization is not involved. In Figure 33 the slant plate lens of Figure 86 is shown converting into flat wave fronts the circular wave fronts of sound waves which originated in the acoustic horn at the left. In Figure 65 we saw how a lens could improve loudspeaker coverage by broadening the beam. The lens employed there was a diverging (concave) slant plate lens (thin at the center and thick at the edge). Path-length lenses are used in several commercially available high frequency loudspeakers.

When we discussed lenses for microwaves we noted that the addition of a full horn extending up to the lens provides a shielding advantage. The radiated microwave energy is confined within the horn until formed into a beam by the lens. The "cross talk" between a transmitting antenna and a nearby highly sensitive receiving antenna is thus greatly reduced. A horn-lens combination employing a slant plate lens is shown in Figure 93. This structure is also an excellent directional radiator and receiver of sound waves, and for this purpose it has certain advantages over parabolic dishes.

Although parabolic dishes are used primarily as microwave antennas, they have sound-wave applications where it is desired to enhance the loudness of distant sounds. In the recording of distant bird songs, for example, use is often made of parabolic reflectors. However, as we noted in connection with Figure 42, the directional properties of the horn used

Fig. 93. A full conical horn feed improves the effectiveness of the slant plate lens for both microwaves and sound waves. For microwaves the horn provides a shielding effect, and for sound waves the directivity is improved when a large spectrum of audio frequencies is involved.

with the parabolic dish strongly affect the effectiveness of the combination. Thus the fixed aperture of the horn causes it to be highly directional at high frequencies and almost non-directional at extremely low frequencies. When high frequencies are radiated by the small feed horn, only the center of the dish is illuminated. When low frequencies are radiated, most of the energy "spills over" the side of the dish because the horn does not have any appreciable directional effect at these frequencies. A similar behavior occurs when the dish and horn are employed as a receiver for distant sounds.

This unwanted effect, caused by efforts to make the unit effective over a wide range of frequencies, is not present in the horn-lens combination of Figure 93 when it is used for sound waves. It provides the maximum directivity possible for its aperture, no matter what the frequency. All sounds, high and low, enter the mouth of the horn, are focused and "funneled" to the acoustic microphone placed at the horn throat.

Rods of Artificial Dielectrics

In the open-structure disk lens of Figure 81 groups of disks were mounted on central rods and the individual rods supported to form the lens. Each such rod can thus be thought of as a cylindrical "chunk" of dielectric, comparable to the cylindrical rod of true dielectric of Figure 49. We noted in connection with Figure 50 that dielectric rods can guide microwaves and, in connection with Figure 46 that they can give radiated microwaves direction.

Figure 94 is a photo of a World War II U.S. radar which had 42 such dielectric rods as radiators in its antenna array. From the equivalent

FIG. 94. This shipboard radar of World War II had an array of dielectric rod radiators for its microwave antenna. (*Courtesy Bell Telephone Laboratories.*)

dielectric lens action of the multiple rows of disks in Figure 81, we can expect that the "disk-studded" rod of Figure 95 should act as a dielectric rod radiator when inserted in a wave-guide "feed" as shown. Figure 96 is a display of the wave fronts of the emerging microwaves from this radiator when photographed by the method described earlier. Without the rod the wave fronts would have been circular, with their center located at the small feed horn at the right. With the rod present the waves are flat, like the flat wave fronts emerging at the right of the lens of Figure 96. The rod thus produces wave fronts whose flat area is much larger in "aperture" than the aperture of the small horn feeding the line. Accordingly, directional "gain" is achieved by the use of the rod.

Practical use of the high directivity gain available in an artificial dielectric rod antenna has been made in the design of television receiving antennas. One highly directional unit is shown in Figure 97. It was employed in New York City to discriminate against the multiple reflections of the transmitted television signals from the many tall buildings. This antenna, aimed in the direction of the strongest signal arrival path, transformed a blurred television picture into a sharp one. In this application only horizontally polarized waves were involved, so that disks could be replaced by horizontal rods. At the long wavelengths used in television a true dielectric rod would have been out of the question, as would a parabolic dish or a lens.

If our rod-supported row of disks is extended indefinitely, a microwave wave guide results, possessing the low loss characteristics of a true dielectric rod wave guide. The long white "wire" in Figure 98 is such a "disk-studded line." As the photo

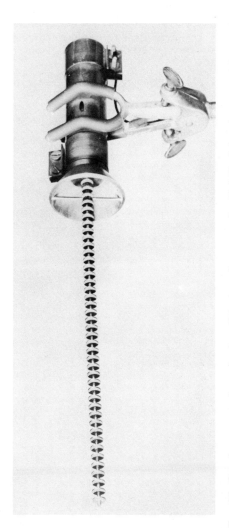

Fig. 95. One long row of conducting disks constitutes an "artificial" dielectric rod end-fire radiator.

Fig 96. The normally circular wave fronts radiated from a small microwave horn are converted to plane wave fronts of sizable extent by the axial disk-on-rod artificial dielectric. The larger flat wave fronts correspond to those from a larger aperture, higher gain horn.

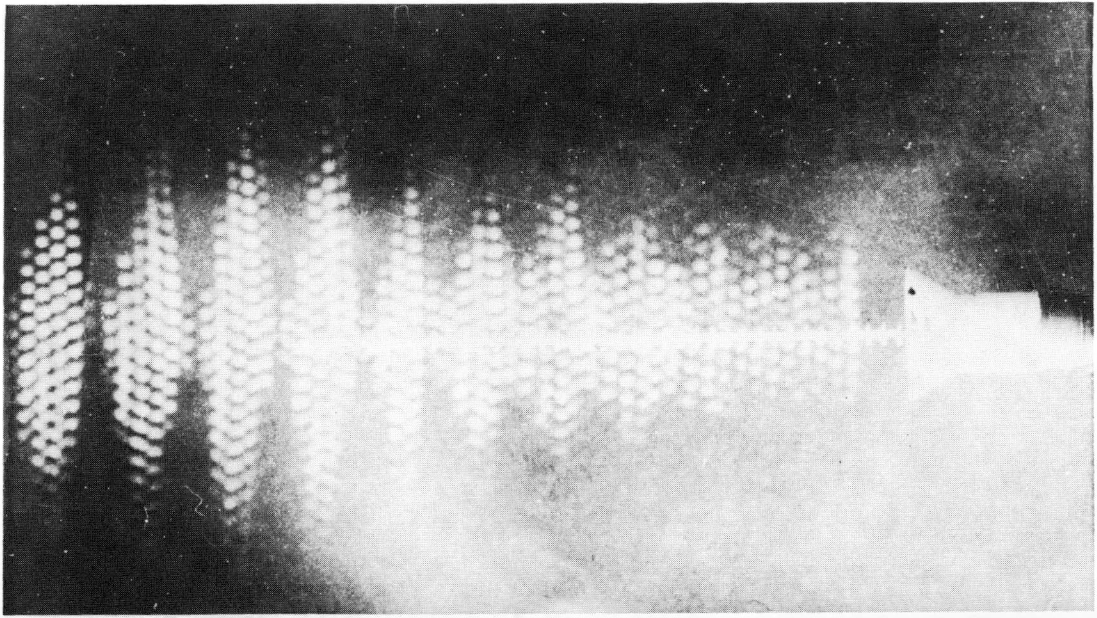

FIG. 97. For the meter-long horizontally polarized television waves, the disk-on-rod artificial dielectric radiator looks like this. As a television receiving antenna, its higher directivity is useful in cities where the "echoes" of television signals reflected from tall buildings normally create annoying "ghosts" that blur the viewer's television picture.

shows, the wire need not be perfectly straight; the curve near the far end is made gradual enough to ensure that the microwave energy is still "bound" to the line. The energy eventually radiates from the end of the line and is picked up by the horn receiver held in the hand of the operator.

Since the open-structure disk lens focuses both microwaves and sound waves, the disk-studded line also can guide both forms of waves. At the time the photo of Figure 98 was taken, both sound waves and electromagnetic waves were being propagated along the line. The white, conical, acoustic horn receiver seen near the far end of the line is substituted for the microwave receiver when it is desired to receive the sound waves.

In both the acoustic and microwave situations the disk-on-rod wave guide is "inside-out" in comparison to the hollow-tube wave guides. The metal part is now at the axis and the wave energy is guided along a region close to and surrounding the rod, instead of within a tube.

Simultaneous Operations
with Sound Waves and Microwaves

We can describe some experiments that demonstrate strikingly the similarity between waves of light and waves of sound. In these experiments two of the devices mentioned in this chapter will be employed to guide or focus sound waves and microwaves simultaneously.

We shall commence with one of the disk-on-rod devices. By means of a tee junction, we can conduct sound waves and microwaves to the round guide which launches the waves onto the metal disk end-fire radiator. This is shown in Figure 99. Both

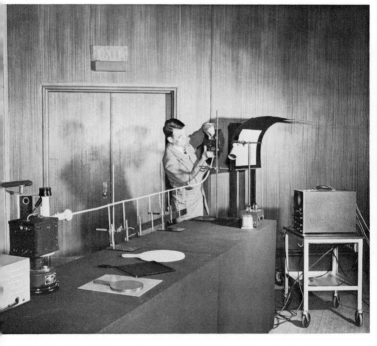

FIG. 98. The disk-on-rod metal dielectric can be extended to very long lengths. The "white wire" in this photo is such a wave guide, capable of carrying both microwaves and sound waves simultaneously.

sound waves and microwaves are then radiated and similar directional patterns are generated for both types of waves. The sound-wave detector (the white round microphone) can be equipped with an amplifier which causes a light to light when loud sound waves strike the microphone. Similarly the microwave detector and amplifier (the rectangular horn) can cause a light of another color to light when strong microwaves strike the detector. If the two detectors are placed in juxtaposition as shown, the simultaneous lighting of the two lights demonstrates the simultaneous presence of the two types of waves.

To show that both types of waves are present, we can block one of the energy forms by placing something in the path of the waves. Thus if the wooden paddle lying on the table is placed in the path, the sound waves are blocked and that light goes out. The microwaves, however, penetrate wood quite well, and the other light remains lit. A metal screen with openings that are small compared to the microwave wavelength can short-circuit the electric field of the microwaves if the conductors are lined up to be parallel to the electric vector. In the photo they are perpendicular to the electric vector and both microwaves and sound waves are unaffected. When the grating is rotated to make the rods vertical, only the sound waves pass through. Again only one light lights, this time the light on the acoustic receiver. The metal sheet shown on the table blocks both the sound waves and radio waves and causes both lights to be extinguished.

We observed that the lens of Figure 86, originally designed for microwaves, focused sound waves also. Simultaneous focusing of both waves can be demonstrated by the experiment sketched in

FIG. 99. A tee junction is used to feed sound waves and microwaves simultaneously to an artificial dielectric rod radiator. The receiver on the right verifies the fact that a wire grid passes only the sound waves, and a wooden paddle only the microwaves; a metal plate stops both.

Figure 100. A sound generator and receiver and a microwave generator and receiver are arranged as shown on both sides of the lens. When the lens is out of the path (at A), the received signals are too weak to cause the indicating lights to light. When the lens is in the proper position, both lights light. When the sound and microwaves have equal wavelengths, the beam width (focal width) of the lens is the same for both waves, and when the lens is moved out of position the lights are extinguished simultaneously.

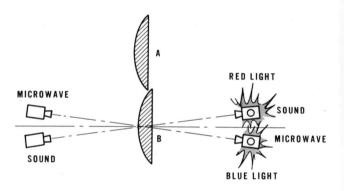

FIG. 100. The same path-length lens simultaneously focuses the sound waves and microwaves radiated by the transmitters on the left.

EPILOGUE

There are several ways one might bring this little discourse on waves to an end. One would be to review the significance of some of the properties of light waves and sound waves we have encountered. For example, our first equation (*wavelength equals velocity divided by frequency*) showed that even though the velocities of propagation of light and sound are vastly different, we can still have equal wave*lengths* in the two phenomena if we select vastly different frequencies. We saw that the ability of an aperture or radiator to form beams depends only on the aperture size measured in wavelengths (*beam width equals $51\lambda/a$*), and *not* on whether the waves are electromagnetic or acoustic in nature. We noted the similarity of both forms of wave motion to water waves spreading out in a pond, even as regards the concept of wave velocity (*phase velocity*) and energy velocity (*group velocity*). We saw that sound waves and microwaves are easy to generate *coherently,* as single-frequency wave trains, but that only recently, following the advent of the laser, has highly coherent light been a possibility. We saw that waves are *diffracted* into shadow areas by the edges of the opaque bodies causing the shadows, and that wave direction can be changed by *refraction,* through the use of prisms or lenses which create a change in the wave velocity. Finally we saw that wave *confinement* (as, for example, the confinement of microwaves in a wave guide) creates unusual energy distributions with accompanying changes in the nature of the wave velocity.

Another way of ending this little book would be to emphasize the parallel relationship between objects that affect or influence the two wave motions. We noted that electromagnetic waves, being electrical in nature, are strongly affected by the presence of electrical conductors, yet hardly notice non-conductors, even walls of brick or wood or stone of immense rigidity. The thin filmy "balloons" of polyethylene plastic, satellites Echo I and II, reflect microwaves because there is incorporated in the plastic an extremely thin electrically conducting layer; television signals can be "bounced" off them back down to earth, thousands of miles away. Sound waves, on the other hand, are not disturbed by electrically conducting screen doors and window screens; they even pass through very thin plastic sheets, whether or not the sheets are "metallized" like the Echo satellites. But a heavy, rigid, wall is something else again for sound waves. So we saw, as did Lord Rayleigh, the correlation between the "conducting" requirement for light waves, and the "rigid" requirement for sound waves.

We might conclude by harking back to the Foreword, to emphasize, again, that by observing similarities and differences we can arrive at new knowledge, new discoveries. We saw that the horn or megaphone, with which early scientists directed sound waves, was the basis for the extremely useful directional horns now extensively employed in the microwave applications. The parabolic reflecting telescopes of astronomy were the basis for parabolic pickup devices for sound waves and, still later, for the "dish" antennas used to focus microwaves. We saw that it was a *recognition* of similarities that led to the first use of wave guides to employ their effect on the wave velocity of microwaves for focusing (Figure 70), just as the difference of the wave velocity of light in glass made possible the focusing of light with glass lenses. It was the knowledge and analysis of how light waves are refracted by the action of the individual molecules of glass that led to the "artificial" dielectric lenses for microwaves. And we learned of the new horizons opening up for the manipulation of visible light waves (now that the coherent light beam of the laser is a reality), just as we now manipulate coherent sound waves and coherent microwaves.

So perhaps our final thought is both our first and our last: "Go and do *likewise!" Where* can a new discovery we have just learned about be simulated elsewhere? *How* is the discovery similar to something in another field? *What* am I aware of in another field that can be a benefit to the new discovery *or* that can benefit *from* the discovery? I have learned that such "cross-fertilization" procedures were successful in the fields of sound waves and light waves. How can *I* do likewise *now?*

FURTHER READING

Donald R. Griffin. *Echoes of Bats and Men*. Science Study Series, Doubleday & Co., Inc., 1959. Especially Chapters 3 and 5.

S. A. Schelkunoff and H. T. Friis. *Antennas: Theory and Practice*. New York: John Wiley & Sons, 1952. Especially Chapters 1, 5, 6, 16, 18 and 19.

E. G. Bowen, editor. *A Textbook of Radar*. Cambridge University Press, 2nd edition, 1954.

H. T. Friis and W. D. Lewis. *Radar Antennas*. Bell System Technical Journal, Vol. 26, pp. 219–317, April 1947.

H. T. Friis. *Microwave Repeater Research*. Bell System Technical Journal, Vol. 27, pp. 183–246, April 1948

Lord Rayleigh. *Theory of Sound*. New York: Dover Publications, 1945.

E. Meyer. *Electro-Acoustics*. London: George Bell & Sons Ltd., 1939.

Arthur H. Benade. *Horns, Strings and Harmony*. Science Study Series, Doubleday & Co., Inc., 1960. Especially Chapters 1, 2, and 3.

Willem A. van Bergeijk, John R. Pierce, and Edward E. David, Jr. *Waves and the Ear*. Science Study Series, Doubleday & Co., Inc., 1960. Especially Chapters 2 and 3.

INDEX

ANCHOR BOOKS

SCIENCE STUDY SERIES

ANCHOR BOOKS

ANCHOR BOOKS